Whiskeyboat

Nick Plumber

≼ *To that fading breed: The cab driver.* ≽

Book layout by Eric Berkow

Portions of section one were published in *303 Magazine* as *"The Steel Coachman"*

The poem *Whiskeyboat* appeared in Modern Drunkard Magazine

Whiskeyboat

I think they've started putting whiskey in the water
so I pour from the faucet
God's own breath
because my fares are all red-eyed savages,
bloody and bruised
Tattooed with lessons unlearned
from fights with parking meters
and battles with windmills of dirt
like freshly paroled inmates from the whiskey barge
they have breath like dragon's teeth
And turpentine skin
And speak a language as old as the grape
As old as Babel
As old as Sin
full of slurs and raspberries,
blasphemies and curses
But I understand you
My gin-soaked Quixotes
And I'll boat you down the river Lethe
To your home
Your street
Your lover
A boatman
in a sea of olives
and broken glass

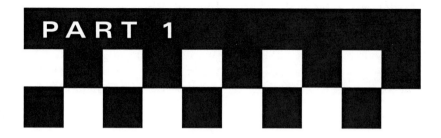

PART 1

I drive. Then I drive some more. Through empty streets and full, mist splitting my headlights, tires singing on asphalt, I drive. Past pools of light spilling onto sidewalks and in bright sun that burns my bleary eyes, I drive. It's like a sixteen-hour road trip but I keep ending up where I started: in Denver. There are spots to hit, people to pick up. Some treat me like a long lost friend, some like a servant. Some nights the shitty music from the radio irritates me, some nights it is a sound track to a Nouveau Scorsese movie that I hope he never makes. (I am the Taxi Driver; should I get a mohawk?)

Tonight it is squealing yoo-hoo girls, drunk yuppies, and douche-bags. The pain hits me in three places; my ankle, that has been doing nothing but "tilt, stop, tilt, stop" for twelve hours, my wrists, that are all carpel tunnel worse than when I did data entry, and my head. My head-like someone is stabbing me right above the eye socket, and then twisting it every time the drunk, overweight, over made up blonde cunt yells: "Oh, my God!!!!". Insert smiley faces, "LOL", eye rolling, inanity, and, I hope, a punch in the gut. I think this job has destroyed any vestige of political correctness that my Boulder, Colorado upbringing had instilled. Blacks from the Points don't tip, Mexicans give me an attitude, like I might mug them, and still don't fucking tip me. Yuppies treat me like the servant they can't afford (but fucking tip), and damn it, only the fat chicks hit on me. Call me an asshole, call me Ishmael, call me everyman, but call my ass so I can pick you up... I'm not proud.

I deal with the stinking dregs of humanity, after the bartender is through, the ex-girlfriend is done, after you've shit yourself, fucked your pimp, or found your connection, I'll pick your ass up off the street and get you to your destination. Don't get me wrong, somewhere in here it sounds like I hate you. I don't...usually. You are my cash cow, my Pimp Pasha, my bread-and-fucking-butter. I only hate you sometimes, or most times...lol... smiley face with tongue...eye roll.

❀◉◎❀

I had a fare the other day, a little slip of a girl, drunk as hell. She was cute, I noticed that at least. That's a good sign, right? Anyway, she stumbled into my cab. Even though I was on another call, I just couldn't throw her out into the night. She was cold, and drunk, and, OK, she was cute. But I just can't say no to a Damsel in Distress, never could. Probably explains why my life is such a mess.

As I drove her up Park Avenue, she turned and asked me if I was going to puke. That threw me for a moment, and, after thinking about it for a second, I responded:

"No, I'm not gonna puke, are you going to puke, honey?"

I know, I know, I'm a sexist pig, I call all drunk women in my cab "honey" or "darlin'" just like I call all drunk men "buddy" or "dude". It's not like I know any of their names, and honestly, I'm not going to spend the time trying to figure them out, unless they become a regular. So, she's so out of it, she thinks that because she's nauseous, that I'm going to puke. Some sort of psychic intestinal resonance, I guess. I start driving faster, because, Damsel in Distress or not, I don't want her puking in my cab. We get to her house and she waves a credit card and some cash at me, meanwhile looking greener and greener all the time. The cash was about two bucks less than the fare, but I went for it instead. Better a two-dollar loss than a front seat full of half digested nachos and beer.

As I drove away, it struck me that the fare had been a metaphor for life, but I just couldn't figure out exactly how. Maybe that we all travel through life in a haze, mistaking our problems for other people's, really unaware of the ride, and the only thing certain and inevitable is the destination. Or, maybe, take what you can get, when you can get it. Or, more likely, the only real message was that girls who weigh 100 pounds shouldn't do tequila slammers.

✿◉◎◉✿

I should probably get to the story. I feel that I am avoiding it... Maybe I'm setting the scene, giving you the feel of the character — me. Or maybe I'm just scared where the story will go, where it's been, what it might become... by telling it, I am giving it credence, a solidity that may come back to haunt me, like- well, maybe I should just tell it.

My day is long, like anyone's I guess. Like a fry cook, a waiter, hell, like a drunk's. Like anyone who wakes up, clocks in, and doesn't expect to be done until it is time to go to bed and start again. Don't get me wrong, there's no ur-lord punching me in the nuts to get to work, I do it to myself, like all truly horrible things. Imagine a day, perhaps the day before bizarre and beautifully strange days happen. I wake up, taste of four am scotch and a shitty burrito in my mouth, my bedroom smells like stale masturbation and cheap laundry. I stand, sporting morning wood, give it the finger, and stumble, bushy haired and booger eyed, naked through my empty house, to the bathroom for an uncomfortable piss. Splashing water in my face, not showering, not shaving, not seeing the point, I dress in the clothes that are on top of the pile and smell the least of spunk and sweat. I brush my hair in a vague and irritated way, think the thousandth time about just shaving it off, and don my beat up straw cowboy hat, my one affectation, or maybe just a way to keep my hair out of my eyes. Still irritated with the night's ghosts, the phantom streets I drove along when I was supposed to be resting, I walk out the door to my demon cab, coffee gripped tightly in my left hand, keys in my right...it is one-thirty in the afternoon.

I book in, I run a few bells- still feeling crusty. Now that I am in the cab I am uncomfortable in my own skin, like some bastard last night painted my nuts with turpentine and wax. The sweat groups on the back of my legs, I feel it settle around my balls, soak into my jeans. Outside it isn't hot yet, just warm. It is nowhere near the point where I have to decide between comfort and gas mileage, I start to think that a shower would be good. But I know, now that I am in the cab, I know I won't stop, except for gas, for flags, for queers, hippies, or drunks, even when I'm hungry and psychotic and I might not even stop. Just pick you up.

The first bell is these two little old ladies. They should be capitalized "Little Old Ladies". I get them once, twice a week, one older than the other, always from the same shitty Colfax diner to their apartment on Garfield. They argue quiet, almost outside normal human perception, an argument that has been going in for years, for decades. I can never figure them out, what are they: mother/daughter, roommates, sisters, lovers? They dote on each other, fight with each other with an old bitter familiarity that could mean any kind of relationship. I respect them because they live in an apartment, and not an assisted living village. I imagine being put out to pasture, belligerent as I am, but alone. And I drive, drive them home. They ignore me, I hear them... they are worth-$6.85, plus, always, a $1.15 tip.

LITTLE OLD LADIES: $8.00

The next fare is a voucher: a cancer patient. There are a few different vouchers: RTD, Logisticare, Medicaid, etc. What it means is that I take injured, crippled, messed up people from point A to point B. No cash, no tips, and the company takes 10%. The foreigners; the Ethiopians, Iranian, Indians, they hate them, they drop them if they can, treat them like dirt. Less money, less respect... I don't care, someone in my cab means money; it's like rolling the dice.

It is a short run, full of pain. Where I become the poor man's sounding board... how the doctor treated him, how his kids treated him, how it hurts to be alive. I am the audio dumping ground, the psychic toilette, the faceless driver with a direct input to God:

register your complaint about life with the higher-ups... There is no need for me to respond, react, interact. Just nod, agree, commiserate, grunt, everything is horrible, and nothing was his fault. Mercifully, I drop him off quickly.

Angry Cancer Patient- $8.70 *Minus corporate 10%:$7.83*

I help him out of the cab, fill out the paperwork, and look at the clock. It's nearing four o'clock. I have until 7:30 to do my inspection and cashier, but cashiering late is always a mess, too many cars, too many cabbies. Putting it into drive, I headed out towards Holly and MLK. I pull into the lot and there are two cars in front of me for inspection. I throw it into park, turn up the radio, and pull the credit card slips and vouchers down from my visor, then pull cash out of the left front pocket of my black denims. It is Wednesday, and I've slacked the last two days. I owe five-thirty on my lease and have $97 all together. I decide to pay $90. I have seven dollars in cash for my bank, my gaslight is on, and I'm hungry. I know that my first two bells would be busts. The first one fuel for the cab, the second fuel for me. Unless the first bells pay with credit cards or are vouchers. Then my bank will go for gas, and I will go hungry for a few bells. It's how it works, I always start a little nervous, uncertain, owing money, with little to show but a day's work ahead of me.

The car in the bay backs out, then drives off, the next one pulls in. We inch forward.

I remember watching movies like Taxi Driver and growing up with the TV series Taxi. The give and take between drivers, the jokes, and hanging out. Even in Scorsese's epic, there was a certain psychotic camaraderie between cabbies, just like any other job. I haven't found it. Maybe it used to be there, but the computer killed it. We no longer talk to dispatch on the radio. We plug in codes and zones, the screen beeps at us, tells us where to go, who to pick up. A one way flow of information.

Another cab pulls up behind me, a hybrid, the mileage is good, but the company charges twenty-five bucks more a day. I haven't figured out if that is a savings yet. A cab pulls out, we pull up. I turn on my lights and pop the hood, I am next.

The only camaraderie I have, the only other cab driver I know, is the son of a bitch who brought me in, who got me the job. We used to play music together, before I gave up, before I got lost in a forest of blonde hair and gray-green eyes.

The next cab pulls out, I pull in, turn the signals left-right, turn my tire. The company mechanic opens my back door, looks for puke or trash (I suppose. He's never said anything but: "Looks good."). He goes around back, I throw it in reverse, flick my blinkers left-right again. He comes around to the driver's side, checks my mile-age-259768, then enters it into the computer. He walks up to the hood, looks at me expectantly. I pull the hood lever again, then shrug. He begins methodically to pound the hood, left to right, with his fist. It pops up, he grins through his beard, opens the hood, and checks a fluid, I think it's transmission fluid. I turn the engine off on cue, he checks the rest of the fluids in rapid succession, slams the hood down, gives me a thumbs up. Three minutes have passed. I know my hood is now pockmarked with greasy fist prints, little Roarsaches of motor oil. I'll wash it tomorrow, and it'll probably happen again. I pull out, find a parking spot, and walk in to the office.

The office is cool, and finally air-conditioned. Tables and brown-tan carpet beside, it is exactly what the founding fathers gave lip service to, but would have crapped themselves over, then gotten the nearest slow boat for Europe, if they would have seen it. A pure melting pot of Ethiopians, Iranians, Afghanis, Russians, Nigerians, Uzbeks, Ethiopians, Iraqis, Indians, Pakistanis, oh…and Americans.

Yeah, us white boys seem few and far between, at least that's what my fares say to me.

"Wow, an American cab driver!" seems to be the general response. Looking around, I can see why they say that. I am one of three Americans in the room, and the only white guy. The majority are Africans, and, of them, most are Ethiopians. I don't know how I can tell this, but at some point I began to be able to separate them from the other Africans, part of it is the look, black, with a bit of Arab…but mostly it's an attitude. Relaxed, like the worst part is behind them, actually you get that from most of the Africans, this attitude like nothing America can throw at them will phase them. They've seen people shot, arms chopped off, rape, murder, and American troops, and they're supposed to be scared of…what? Some ghetto dime store Dillenger who wants their cash? Not likely, they've been through hell, and this is the fucking promised land. They laugh, seem cheerful all of the time, and, somehow, I feel less of a man around them, these men who have been through hell.

It makes me wonder a bit, why less whites drive. It is a sketchy job, mostly cash, and at night, a prime cash machine for lowlife's with weapons. That could be it, maybe at heart we're a bunch of pussies. My friends have tried to talk me into owning a gun; I honestly couldn't see having it, using it. Maybe a wild shot over my shoulder, maybe shoot myself in the foot. Either way, I shouldn't own a gun. Not at this point in my life, not with everything. It would sit in my desk drawer like a cobra, some vile metal snake, but with a voice. While I slept it would call me, while I sat, sleepless, and watched the sun come up it would talk to me in a seductive metallic voice: "It's easy…be done." It would dance, all cobra gun metal blue, and dare me to dance with it. It would be all too easy; that seductive machine voice, so it stays at the gun shop, and I take my risks with muggers and crack heads…maybe it's one in the same.

I take a number, punch into the computer, and lean against the wall. Don't want to get too comfortable, might imply that I actually want to be here, someone might line jump me, and I want to get the hell out of here and get back on the road. Make me some money, or, more likely, make them some money. I am about fourth in line. The woman hidden behind bullet proof glass waves me forward, she's the cute one, the young one with the tattoos. I smile, flirt a little, feeling like I'm waving my cock at a mermaid in a fish tank, then pass her my vouchers and credit cards, she adds them up, and I pass her a little bit of money. She prints up my receipt, passes it to me and tells me to drive safe. Sometimes I'm tempted to put a crazy look on my face and threaten to mow down every motherfucker who gets in my way. But, then again, I need my job…ain't that a joke?

Getting back into my cab, I start it up, snap my seat belt into place, and "book in". You see, the city is split up into "zones"; areas with a number attached to them. Each cab company numbers them different, but the concept is the same. Capitol Hill is 111, Five Points is split between 110 and 106, and Globeville, where no one really wants to go, not even those hardcore African motherfuckers, is 301. If you live in 301, good luck, if you live in 301 and you are black, take the fucking bus, because the Africans hate poor no tipping surly black folk even more than whitey does. I take calls there when it is slow, never when it is busy, and never at night. For me it is the chance of a knife or gun at my neck and no tip that turns me off. For the Africans, I think it is the no tip part more than anything, that and I think they feel that ghetto blacks make them look bad. There is no love lost between African-Americans and just plain Africans.

The Office is in 311, next to 110, above 301, and about ½ zone from 111. I book into 111. It is a zone I know, live in, and popular zone, mostly young types who drink a lot and tip well, my back yard. Because it is a good zone, I am fifth in line, but I am sure I will have a fare by the time I get there, maybe while I am in transit. Sure enough the computer starts beeping at me. I accept the fare and the name and address pop up. Some guy on Marion Street. Could be a work call, or some guy going to a bar. I try to remember if there is a baseball game, then give up. You get what you get, the fare will be what it will be. I'm barely out of the lot, and it'll take me at least fifteen minutes to get to the fare, if traffic is worse, maybe longer. That's when they start calling another cab company, or give up and walk. I drive fast, avoid Colorado in the hopes that York will not be as congested. MLK drives good, the lights are few and far between. On York the lights seem off, and I'm pissed as I accelerate then stop, over and over. 13th is a dream as always-timed lights, drive 33 miles an hour and it's green all the way, unless you're behind some asshole who doesn't know this. One ignorant lead foot can screw it up for everyone.

I punch in a five-minute warning into the computer, which means the fare gets an automated call. Hopefully I time it well enough so the fare is waiting outside, and I don't lose any time waiting. I slow down as I pull onto his block looking for an address, then see him standing on the curb, a tall guy, dark hair, wearing typical waiter gear; white shirt, black pants. Perfect, service industry types are great fares, good tippers, and always cash. I pull up, he hops in. He names a high-end restaurant downtown. I nod and name the cross streets. We pull off and head down 13th, then to Lincoln, then to 18th, which runs better than 15th, by the way. He isn't very talkative, and I don't feel like striking up a conversation. We hit all the lights, quick and easy. I drop him, hand him my card, and book back into 111.

Bob the Waiter- $7.85 plus a generous tip: $15.00

Even though I'm low on gas, I make a quick loop through Lodo and look for a flag. Down Larimer to 15th, circle the bars and restaurants on Market, then up 17th and out of downtown. No one flags me down, so I head back to Cap Hill and hit a gas station. I drop ten bucks on gas, no more. When I'm flush, later in the night, I'll put in fifteen, maybe twenty. I don't want a full tank of gas, I learned that early on, when I filled up and the cab promptly broke down. When they fixed it, some other cabbie got a full tank of gas, free of charge. Never again, I'd rather risk running out of gas than lose forty bucks. Us cabbies, we're cheap SOB's. Now I have a thirteen-dollar bank, and me stomach, it's a rumbling. I'm still fourth in queue so I cruise up Seventeenth, past the restaurants and gay bars, hoping someone is done with an early dinner, tired of a boring happy hour, or just plain day drunk. No dice, I circle the block, pass by another gay bar, cruise up Washington to Colfax, turn up the longest street in America, drive slowly past a few hippie bars, then give up and park in the lot of Charlie's Laundromat. There's always the question of drive or sit. On a slow day, I'll cruise around for a bit, then give up, park it, and read. It's a matter of burning gas and still getting no fares. If the town seems hopping, I'll cruise around for fares, if not, I sit. I could go downtown and sit in front of a hotel with about a hundred other cabbies, but that never seems to work for me. I'll finally get a call after waiting a good half hour with no one coming out of the hotel, then I waste time and gas getting back to Cap Hill. So I park it, besides we all need some downtime, right? I know later on, once the drunks come out, I'll be too busy to piss or eat, so I might as well enjoy some it now. I pull out a book and start reading.

I get a fare about ten minutes later, nothing to write home about, just taking a quiet guy from point A to point B. Could be a drug run, it could be a tryst, could be nothing. The life of a cabbie is huge periods of boredom spiked with occasional chaos, fear, and entertainment, just like everyone, I guess. After two hours and a quick lunch I'm thirty bucks up and a little scared. It's too damn slow and I owe the cab company, the mortgage company, the utilities, and my ex-wife a shitload of cash. Slow or not, I start circling with the other sharks around Lodo, sweating and cursing all the assholes who insist on driving downtown.

Three hours later the bar rush has started and I'm in the zone: pick up on Cap Hill drive downtown, pick up an early drunk, drive them back to Cap Hill…and so on. I want to count my money to know how I'm doing, but it's too busy. All the fares run into each other, I've got to piss, I'm hungry, and I'd kill for a beer, but I ain't stopping for anything. I'm thrown off the zone by a gaggle of girls who want to go to the bars in Wash Park. It's a good fare: about fifteen plus tip, but then I have to decide whether to book into the area, which is hit or miss, or burn the time and gas to get back to 111. I check the number of fares in the surrounding zones, and decide to drive back to 111 since there's a good gas station with a bathroom along the way. I gas up with twenty bucks so I don't have to stop for the rest of the night, take a piss, think about coffee and decide against it. A cup now and I'll be up till five in the morning tossing and turning. I do some perfunctory stretching and hop back in the cab, book in and hit a fare right away, back into the fray. The night blurs into streetlights, honking horns, and lilac perfume. Smeared sensations of the road, the sound of my tires on pavement and the smell of the young goddesses in my backseat who won't give me the time of day. Two o'clock rolls around and I'm no longer booking in, just trolling the streets for drunks, circle the block here, drive there, pull over there with a squeal of tires, off into the night the coachman of the dark with my carriage of vinyl and steel. Around two-thirty

I'm done, kaput, eyes gummed up, wrist sore, legs cramped. I'm driving up Twentieth swearing I won't pick up another soul, be they billionaire or supermodel.

She's standing in front of this odd Victorian looking building that houses a porn store. Green and black hair, schoolgirl skirt, striped green thigh-highs. A candy raver lost in the late night Lodo landscape of jocks and socialites, a waif on the roadside. Before I know it, I pull over, some autonomous reaction to the hand flailing hopelessly in the air, some gut boner reaction to the outfit and the hair. She runs to the cab, and piles in breathlessly.

"Thanks for stopping," she says.

"Sure," I mean it's my fucking job after all.

"My boyfriend, was supposed to pick me up," there's a brief pause, then a muttered: "asshole."

"No problem, where we going?"

She laughs a little, sounding tired and small.

"Right, sorry, um, Twelfth and Marion."

"Right-o." I put it in drive and head up Twentieth, at least it's on the way home.

"I like your hat," she says.

"Thanks," I adjust it a little self-consciously and try to catch her eye in the rearview mirror, she is looking out the window, just a bit sadly.

"Do you like driving a cab?"

"Sometimes," I shrug, make the turn onto Broadway, "get to meet a lot of interesting people, the money's not to bad."

"See a lot of strange things?" She looks and smiles at me tentatively.

"Yeah, more than my fair share, I guess, not as much as you'd think." She waits for an example, but for some reason, I'm not in a storytelling mood, the night's too quiet, I'm too tired, but I feel like

I should say something. Like she's waiting for me to say something, anything. The right thing. "What do you do?"

"I work in a wacker booth at that porn store back there." She snorts derisively.

I laugh a little, hopefully not in a mocking way.

"Bet you meet your share of interesting people."

"Not as many as you'd think," she leans forward and I get a whiff of something exotic and subtle. "It's up here on the left."

I pull over and stop the meter, she fumbles with her cash and leaves me a four-dollar tip.

"Thanks again for picking me up."

I hand her my card. "No problem, feel free to call me if you get abandoned again." I smile, she meets my eyes for a moment, then looks away.

"Sure," she looks at my card, "thanks again."

She gets out and I watch her walk away and to her door, maybe thinking of lost opportunity, lost chances, ships in the night, but more thinking with my crotch. I sigh and put into gear, feeling sad and that somehow I missed something subtle and important. I turn up the radio, head up Fourteenth to the edge of Capitol Hill and the empty house I call home.

I park the cab down the block, grab my cell, water bottle, credit card receipts, and sunglasses, and get out. I'm slightly unsteady on my feet like a man long at sea. I get my land legs and walk to my house, dark like all the other ones on the block, lawn gone to seed, maybe in need of a paint job. I open the door, turn on the lights and empty my pockets onto the dining room table, I straighten and sort crumpled bills, add up my credit card receipts and vouchers, and pour myself a tall glass of scotch. A decent night, about two fifty. I split off my bank, and my lease money, put the rest back in my pocket, and walk up stairs. The house is quiet and I can hear the night breathing down my neck, stifling and hot. I look in the empty room at the end of the hall, the small bed, the posters on the wall, and wonder where my boy is tonight. Asleep, tucked in warmly by his mom, a thousand miles away. Does he dream of me? I sit on his tiny bed with its light coating of dust and listen to the ghosts roam the empty house downstairs, knowing sleep won't come easy tonight. I get up and go back downstairs before I break down completely, I pour myself another glass of scotch, deep as country wells, sit in a chair, and gaze out my living room window, waiting for the sunrise to come.

❀◉◎❀

I met Mary, all five foot ten of her, dirt blonde hair, laughing gray-green eyes:
- ◉ at a church social
- ◉ at the grocery store
- ◉ bowling

We had all sorts of stories, we laughed over them. Maybe a chance meeting at the chiropractors, or we sat next to each other on a crowded bus. She wanted a good story that rang true, just a bit romantic, but not one of those squishy lovey dove ones that makes the couple go "oooh" and the crowd feel slightly nauseous. She was like that, my Mary, wanting to reinvent the past to make the present more solid. I just went along, enchanted. It wasn't like she was lying, she just wanted to get it together for when our son would ask. The truth was a little rougher, a lot drunker, and slightly uncouth.

I met her at a punk concert, loud music, lots of beer, I was covered in sweat and bleeding slightly from a good hit in the mosh pit. She was in the front screaming, I spilled her beer, she called me an asshole. Later, I saw her at the bar, apologized, bought her a beer, and went home with her. No good lesson about romance, sobriety, and safe sex. So...we met at:
- ◉ the zoo
- ◉ a coffee shop where we both wanted the last cheese Danish

And so on. In reality, I fixed her breakfast in my Cap Hill one room efficiency, a bit dirty, a place where you could hear the neighbor kill himself quietly, with battered books on dumpster dived bookshelves, and local rock posters. She loved that I could cook, I walked her home, then... nothing. I was busy with the band, and chasing everything that moved. To be honest, not much of a nice guy. I ran into her at a bar a few months later, she called me an asshole again, I apologized again, we went home again. Rinse, lather, repeat. We went out a few more times, and I found that I couldn't get her off my mind, I was falling in love and it scared the hell out of me. Eventually, I bowed to the inevitable, and we moved in together. A few years later, I popped the question, since it seemed like the right thing to do. So, we met:

- at the theater
- skydiving
- at the museum

It's not that she hated the truth, it's just that she thought that the truth should be better. And I went along because I couldn't say no to her.

✿ ◉ ◉ ✿

I wake up in the chair, uncomfortable, a crick in my neck, with the mostly empty bottle of scotch beside me. I stand, try to work the crick out of my neck, and hobble upstairs to my room. I'm too young to feel this old. I strip, tossing my clothes into a pile. Laundry is coming up, and I'll have to take a few hours away from the cab to do it. I find it hard to get motivated to do it, once I'm up I just feel the cab calling, telling me I'm not making money, in fact I might be losing money just sitting there watching the clothes turn in the dryer. Naked, I crawl into bed, rearrange the rumpled covers and try to fall back to sleep. I can hear the town waking up around me, people rushing to work, straightening ties, having breakfast at a normal time, with their normal families. I turn on the electric fan by my bed, drowning out normalcy, shield my eyes from the sunlight leaking into the room, and somehow convince myself to drift off.

❀ ◎ ◎ ◎ ❀

I'm driving, even in my dreams. Mary sits next to me, cold cup of coffee in her hand.

"Why don't you go look for work today?"

"I will, I will," I say as we turn onto Colfax, not the real street, but some sort of uber-Colfax, an amalgam of everything that Colfax is, bars, hookers, strange shops.

"Well, then do it," she says. It's an old argument by this time, one we go through every day, like robots stuck on a self-destruct sequence. I look over and she's not in the passenger seat anymore, and I drive on up Colfax, alone. I know, even while sleeping, that the symbolism is obvious, and that I'll know that when I wake up. In the meantime, I keep driving through blurred candy colored streets, always a little bit late for the next fare.

❀ ◎ ◎ ◎ ❀

Thursday. I wake up thinking: Thursday. It's the beginning of the weekend, and there's an early ball game, good money. I lay there for a while, trying to make everything focus, tasting the peat of a good scotch hangover, then get up. Time to make the fucking donuts. Knowing that I probably reek of scotch, I climb in the shower and blast it hot, as hot as I can take, then cold, then hot again. Good old-fashioned shock therapy. I fix some coffee, and check my email. Mostly junk, a reminder that my cell phone bill is due, and a bitchy email from Mary about the child support. Great. I think about what I owe everyone, and realize that I'll be working 14 hour shifts through the weekend, hell through Tuesday, and I'll still probably owe on my lease, not to mention my mortgage. I think again about selling the place or at least getting roommates, but it seems like such a huge step, a final step. I realize that somewhere deep down, deeper than rational thought, I think she'll still come back, that they'll still come back. Closing my email, I vow, for the umpteenth time, to start asking around, maybe put an ad up somewhere, to get off my ass and find a roommate, to do something. I finish my coffee, fill up my water bottle, and head out to my cab.

I book in while I arrange my things and do a quick inspection of my cab. I find an empty pint glass in the back seat, pull up the cushions, hoping to find cash, although usually all I find are quarters, bar napkins, and the occasional piece of jewelry or cell phone. Oh, and once a bag of kind bud that I gave the mechanics at the shop. They loved me for that one. I decide that I can go another day without washing her, start her up, and drive to the nearest gas station. I try to keep an eye out for cheap gas, but at this point there's no such thing, just pull up, and bend over at the pump. I put in the minimum, ten bucks, even though I'm temporarily flush with cash. I leave the door open while I fill up so I can hear the beep from the computer when I get a fare. My first fare is a run to Coors Field, I've got my own route that avoids heavy pre-game traffic and drops the fare right by the box office. I'd tell you, but then every asshole will use it, negating my careful research. I manage to get three fares in before they shut me out of the computer. It's a hassle, when you start they say you have until seven to drop your money for the lease. What they don't tell you is that if you are even a dollar behind they won't let you use the computer until you come in, usually you can work until four or maybe five if you are lucky. I'm not too mad since I managed to get some of the pre-game crowd. I drive out, do my inspection, pay them two hundred, talk to the manager on duty to get reinstated, a pissant maneuver they make you go through. A kind of "please, sir, can I have some more?" thing. I've never seen them tell a driver that he can't drive because he owes them too much money, hell, they want money just as bad as you, just want you to know who's in charge, I guess. I get back in my cab, book in to Cap Hill and head out into the evening, a shark after so much chum.

❀☉◉❀

We had our son Mark about two years into the marriage. I thought with Mary's name we should have called him Jesus, but she didn't think that even remotely funny. He came along with the usual terrors, trepidation, and anticipation that comes with every birth, especially a couple's first. I was there when he was born, no pacing father, chain-smoking cigarettes. Instead I stood there in the room telling Mary to fucking breath, while she crushed my hand and filled the air with curses. Birth seems like murder at some deep primeval level, full of pain and tears, born of blood. At least until Mary relented and asked for the damn drugs. She was in labor for what seemed like hours, while I stood by, queasy and nervous, and then- a screaming bundle of muck covered joy. My emotions at that point are kind of hard to explain, a strange combination of terror and joy. Things had changed, and change is always scary. I tried to focus on my job even harder, for once I needed the job, I had to grow up; I had a family. The feeling floated around that now everything had changed, that from now on things would be different, bigger somehow.

We bought a house in a decent neighborhood, not great, but decent. We figured that once Mark was old enough to go to school we could move someplace with a better school system. In the meantime we could afford the mortgage, and we both had that inherent distaste for all thing Suburban that long time hip inner city types have. Strip malls, Stepford wives, fat suburbanites mowing their lawns in Bermuda shorts and black socks, that sort of thing. I remember after we closed on the house, the first night we spent there, I sat up for a while after she and Mark had gone to bed, a rare moment between nursing, screaming, and diaper changes. The house was quiet and creaky even then when it was full of people and hope. I sat on the couch among the boxes and detritus of moving and listened to the house breath and creak, and thought: "Mine. Wow, mine. I own a fucking house." It was good feeling, warm and full of hope. I sat there in silence for a good fifteen minutes, when I finally remembered the warm bed, warm wife, and my husbandly duties as bed filler and comfort bringer. Sometimes I think that's the only time I've ever been truly happy, truly whole. Other times I think it might have just been an illusion, a cop out, a bowing to the image that society and life tries to build for us. But I only think that in the dark, when the night talks to me, mocks me, in a voice old as time, creaky with gun oil and death. Usually, usually, I take the first view, the sunny view, the view to treasure and reassure.

✿ ◉ ◎ ◉ ✿

The day goes, like so many others, in a blur. The baseball game adds to the chaos, the madness, the money. There is a brief bit of beauty and strangeness in my night, one of those fares I know I'll be talking about to entertain my fares, and make the bartender laugh down at the local. I'm waiting at the cabstand in front of Coors Field, second in line. In front of me is a hybrid cab, painted bright green. I see the midgets as they walk out of the crowd up to the hybrid, there's five of them, they look like they could be a family. They say something to the woman driving the hybrid, then shrug and walk back to my cab.

"Can you take five?" he asks me. I hesitate for a moment, just the briefest of a moment. We aren't supposed to take five people in our cabs, but that's not what makes me hesitate, I ignore that all of the time. I feel kind of bad, but what makes me hesitate is that I want to say, "well... sure, you'll fit, you're midgets after all." But customer service and the desire not to offend overtakes my sick sense of humor.

"Yeah, pile in," is all I say. We drive away from the game, and all is fine, me with five midgets in the car, slightly odd, but nothing too strange. We talk about the game, their visit, as I take them to their hotel. Then it happens. Metallica comes on the radio, and they all start singing along, devil horns and all. Suddenly, life is just too surreal, almost too surreal for me to keep a straight face. I mean, five midgets is one thing, five Metallica singing midgets throwing devil horns, well that's something altogether different. Something epic, something bizarre worthy of stories at the bar and around campfires for ages. If only I can keep a straight face long enough to drop them off, get paid, and not offend anyone. The song ends right as I pull into the parking lot of their hotel. They get out, and tip me well. They're a generous folk, I think, cursing myself again, and drive off. Once I'm out of sight, I pull over and laugh for a solid five minutes. Good thing I play poker. The night suddenly seems so much brighter for the oddity.

❀◉◎◉❀

Jody and Ted moved in next door when Mark was about two. A bright, cheerful couple, rock climbers with dogs, transplanted rural hippie types. For some reason we got along great. Being a hardcore city dweller, I wasn't used to being over friendly with the neighbors. In all the apartment buildings I lived in, with thin walls, and noisy plumbing, you were already stuck in everybody's business. The couple fighting next door, the man quietly dying across the hall. You'd nod in the hallways, avoiding conspicuous eye contact, turn sideways in the narrow hallways, you never wanted to know the people all that much because you knew way too much about them just from the noise of daily living. Then I moved into Five Points, what passes as a bad neighborhood in Denver. The blacks who lived on my block didn't want to know what a bunch of white boys were doing in the ghetto, and we didn't want to pay too much attention to what our neighbors were doing. Sometimes it was just healthier to turn a blind eye to the guy on the corner, the guys on the porch, the excess foot traffic in and out of the run-down house next door. Urban living demands a certain amount of "mind your own fucking business" and I figured that out pretty early on.

Mary, of course, would have nothing to do with that attitude, we were a family, we owned a house, we should have neighbors, we should be part of the neighborhood. Gentrification is part of the urban landscape and we were to be part of it. She brought them a welcome to the neighborhood cookie basket of all things, it made me nervous, it felt like we were just one quick step from suburban life and all that that entailed. First we'd welcome the neighbors with cookie baskets, then we'd sign a covenant, complain about the way the people across the street mowed their lawn and painted their house, then go out for a special dinner at the fucking Olive Garden. Of course I kept all this to myself, I'd been married to Mary long enough to know what a dim light she viewed my morose humor on the subject of impending normalcy.

Luckily, Ted and I hit it off right away. The ladies chatted in the living room and he and I sat on the back porch drinking beer. Score one for normalcy. He was a carpenter, a stoner, and, as I said before, a rock climber. I was an insurance salesman, didn't know one end of a hammer from the other, and bowling was about as sportsman-like as I ever got, and that in a sarcastic/ironic sense. For some reason that worked. He would help me out with the small repairs that came with home ownership, I would return the favor, but in a much less skilled manner. Somewhere in there I learned to hang drywall and frame a door, but, as always, with very little skill. Mary would smoke him up, I'd buy the beer, we'd grill, or have them over for dinner. Very normal, almost Norman Rockwell, except for the pot, the microbrews, and the punk rock soundtrack.

❀◎◎◎❀

The rest of the night goes smoothly, a solid stream of pick-ups and good tips, around one I decide to call it for the night, my pockets are jammed with crinkled bills, and I just don't feel like driving anymore. All that I can think of is how good a beer would taste. I was in the zone so much, I didn't think to stop and get beer before the liquor stores closed. I'm tempted to keep driving, rake up as much cash as I can, but truth be told, I'm sick of driving, sick of the people, sick of everything. All I want is a cold beer and a barstool. I figure I can get in at least two before last call. I park the cab in front of my house, drop off all but forty of my cash, and hustle to my local. It is a dimly lit neighborhood bar, nothing fancy. I find an empty barstool and sit down. Josephine, the bartender, sees me and gives me a cheery hello.

"How's business?" she asks as she pours me a beer.

"Good enough, finally told my cab to fuck off." It's an old and worn out joke, but she still smiles. I order a Jameson to go with the beer, might as well turbo-charge the night. I only have a half an hour left to get my buzz on, kill the sore muscles, make the night seem brighter and softer at the same time. The whiskey goes down, burning, I soothe my throat with the dark ale, and relax minutely. Josephine sees this and smiles.

"Rough night?"

"Strange night," I reply and proceed to tell her about the Metallica midgets. By the end of the story she is laughing openly, and I'm ready for another beer and another whiskey. As she pours I look her over. I've known her for years, even before I met Mary. We used to play at the same bars in different bands. She's pretty in kind of a distracted way, if you know what I mean. I wonder why I never tried to hit on her. I think briefly about it, then decide against it. I'm just not ready, and it'd probably just fuck up a good longstanding friendship. I manage to cram down two more beers and two more whiskeys, let the chatter of the bar wash over me, calm me. I return a few hellos, enter into a little small talk, but generally maintain my isolation in a sea of faces. My calmness in the storm. I finish my last beer, a little late for last call, then make my unsteady way home, through the dark, the tall trees, and the lonely oasis of the streetlights.

❀◉◉❀

It had been a bad fight, her screaming, me screaming, the baby crying. Mary had gone upstairs to quiet and comfort Mark, with a final "look what you did" yelled over her shoulder at me. I paced the living room wanting desperately to smash something, somebody, maybe pull my hair out in frustration. Instead I walked out the back door and sat on the stoop, head in my hands.

I felt a tap on my shoulder, and restrained from snarling like a dog. I looked over and saw Jodi's bare, tan legs. I followed them up, past cut off shorts and dirt stained tank top, to her face, then down to the gardening gloves holding two cold microbrews. She smiled and handed me one.

"Here," she said, "I bet you need this."

I took it, and she clinked bottles with me and took a quick sip off of hers.

"Rough one, huh?" She raised an eyebrow, and I nodded, then took a long pull of my beer.

"Yeah," I looked down at the moisture beading on the glass and tugged absent-mindedly at the paper label, "it seems like there's a lot of them lately. Sorry you had to overhear that."

"No problem," she replied looking away at the gnarled peach tree in our back yard. "Ted and I, we're more the quiet fuming type, than the yelling type, but I get it." She took a long drink and looked at me. "Sometimes I wish it was the other way, maybe we'd get it out, you know?"

I laughed shortly and drank some more, feeling the cold beer slide down my throat and the clean bite of the hops.

"Either way it sucks." I paused, then felt the words forcing themselves out. "Sometimes... sometimes, when I'm driving home from work, I just want to keep going, just keep on driving. Empty the bank account, and just drive until I hit the sea. And then, I don't know, turn right or left, up to Canada, down to Mexico, just drive until there's no more land. And then..." I took a long pull off the beer and wiped my mouth with the back of my hand. "And then, maybe I'd just get out of the car and swim. Swim until I can't any more, till my arms fail and the breath leaves me, and I sink. Sometimes I think that I could just do that." I realized that there were tears in my eyes, and I wiped them away fiercely. Jodi put her arm around me and squeezed, just once.

"Yeah," she said softly, "sometimes we all feel like that. But we never do it, do we."

"No," I replied quietly, "we never do." She dropped her arm and upended the bottle.

"Well," she stood up, and wiped her eyes, the gloves left a smudge of dirt on her face, "I guess I'd better get back to weeding the garden."

"Yeah," I replied, raising my beer in a half-toast, "thanks for the beer."

"Any time." She touched my shoulder lightly then walked off, and, I have to admit, I watched her go.

✿◉◎◉✿

I started taking random notes a few months back. I've never been a writer and the only thing artistic I've ever done was play guitar in a punk band, not that I was very good. Hell that's why I played punk. The guitar still sits there in my living room on its stand gathering dust, a kind of mute insult to any artistic endeavor I might contemplate. So these notes, they pile up, I stick them to the fridge, and when they start overwhelming the fridge, crowding out the pictures, silly magnets, and the few crayon drawings that I have from Mark, I take them down, put them in a shoe box, and stick the damn thing in the closet. I have a feeling that it's a sign of my impending mental breakdown or something. The notes don't make much sense to even me. Just: "burn the eyes from the bobble headed St. Christopher on my dashboard" or "their money smells of roses and rot". I guess there's a poem there somewhere, but what the hell would I do with a fucking poem, anyway? But I get these random thoughts rolling around in my head, driving alone, with the radio blasting, no one in the cab but me, no one in my head but me. They'll hammer and hammer away at me, until I have to stop and write them down. I finally broke down and got a pack of sticky notes, and I write the random thought on the sticky note, then slap it on the interior of my glove box. I wonder what a cop would think if he pulled me over and went through the cab, opened the glove box and there it is jammed with notes like: "They laid him out on a rack made of lost car keys and broken turn signals, branded him with red hot hubcaps, and whipped him with gleaming steel antennae." Straight to the fucking nut house, most likely. So I try not to think too much about the habit, but it's hard, coming home drunk from the bar at two in the morning, going for a tasty late night snack, and my twitchy madness stares me smack in the face. I probably should just write them down, then throw them right out, like a sort of mental house cleaning. But for some reason I just can't do it, so I have a fucking closet full of note packed shoe boxes, a sticky note covered fridge, and a glove box packed with paper. Go figure. I haven't snapped yet, at least.

❈ ◉ ◎ ❈

When we bought the house, I was working as an insurance sales-man, which shows just how far you can get with that old college degree. Cultural anthropology, what the fuck was I thinking? Might as well have gotten a degree in under water basket weaving or political science. The job paid well, was tedious, and slightly horrific.

"What's that, Mrs. Jones? You're sixty, have health problems, and no group coverage? No problem... Let me just see here, oh, right, can't help you, have good day."

Some days I felt fine, other times I came home feeling like I should scrub out my soul. But I had a wife, a house, and a newborn. Nose to the grindstone, even if you feel like you're dying a little bit each day, staring at the computer monitor, calling strangers, giving corporate presentations to people who were even more drone like and dead inside as you. I was making the most money I'd ever made, but we were still stretching the budget skin tight. My student loans were coming due, the mortgage was due every month, and a newborn requires an insane amount of everything.

So, I'd get up way earlier than any human being should, climb into my beat up Dodge van, a leftover from the music days, drive to work, straighten my tie, pour myself a cup of coffee, sit down in my cozy cubicle, and sell, sell, sell. For God and Country, for Wife and Child, for House, Home, and Student Loans.

I started getting a bad feeling, well a worse than normal feeling, about year two into the job. Mary was working nights, I was working days. We saw each other on the weekends, and I saw Mark in the mornings, and evenings. Insurance rates seemed to be skyrocketing, my clients weren't renewing as often, especially after they saw the fifty percent increases. More and more business were trying to shift the cost off onto the employees, and there were disturbing rumors going around the office about corporate takeovers, insurance investigations, and the CEO's private bailout plan. Things weren't looking good. I could see a disaster coming, but I didn't know what to do, so I just kept going.

I was beginning to feel the soul killing futility of it all. Mary and I were fighting more and more, the axe was beginning to fall at work and people were running for cover. Sex had left our relationship, and we didn't know what to do about it, so we fought more, about bills, about time together, hell, about what to have for dinner. It wasn't my best time, my shining time, but then I was just trying to keep it together. Ted and I spent more and more time on the back porch drinking beer, and trying to pretend that things weren't falling to pieces around us.

✿ ☉ ☉ ◎ ✿

It's finally Friday, and I'm actually glad. It's time to make money, a guaranteed busy night. Thursday was good, but Friday is always better. I drive straight out to the cab company to pay and do inspection. I don't want to get in the zone, then get thrown off my rhythm by having to book out and pay. The week wasn't so bad, I still owe about 190 on my lease, which means I'll be free and clear and actually making money by about ten o'clock, then the rest of the night is my money, as well as the next two days. Might be able to actually pay off most of what I owe. It puts me in a rare good mood. Then I start driving.

My first few fares go smoothly, then I realize just how drunk out it is. The suit and tie after work happy hour crowd are unusually plowed. I try to remember if it's a full moon as the drunk urban professional, tie slightly askew, cabernet stain marking his starched white shirt, slides his hand up his giggling coworker's skirt, and slathers her face with saliva. She grunts and rubs a manicured hand against his wine stained chest. I turn the mirror. Away. I really don't need to watch that. But, happy in their drunken lus,t they tip well. The drunken yuppie gives me a conspiratorial wink as he pays me.

There's a brief break between the happy hour crowd and the beginning of the bar rush, I stop at a shitty fast food joint and eat in my cab, waiting for a call. I get most of the food down when I get a call. I finish the burger on my way to the pick-up, trying not to spill it down the front of my shirt, and mostly succeeding. Not that it matters, I could probably have half a sandwich stuck to the side of my face and no one would notice as long as it was the side that didn't face the passengers.

The fare is four whoo-hoo girls on their way down to Lodo. They've obviously been pre-bar pumping, slightly tipsy, and loud as hell. They're tarted up and, of course, like my hat. They scream and giggle the whole ten-minute drive downtown, and it's like a weight lifted off my back when they get out, like a calming breeze, or a deep breath. But they tip well. I cruise downtown looking for some early quitters, but the night's too young for that and I get a call. I head pell-mell through downtown, cursing the poorly timed streetlights. The night is full of drunks, plowed and plastered, tried and true, like they're putting whiskey in the water. I get one puker, but pull over just in time, as she heaves her guts into the street. I calmly stretch, and laugh at her a little bit with her friends, offer her a breath mint then get them the hell out of my cab as quickly as possible. I was lucky on that one; no need to push it in case there's a reccurrence.

For once the music on the radio seems to fit my pace, hard rock and some punk helping me drive, feel the groove. I get to the best part of the night, where it all flies by. Pick 'em up drop 'em off, roll roll roll. I get a good crowd of drunks who are actually funny, and I join in the joking. One good belly laugh helps the night along, you feel a little more refreshed and excited.

It's winding down when I get a call from a regular, he's in what I call "Drop Zone Lodo" anywhere near the baseball stadium. At last call it's a madhouse, people diving at the cab, screaming, hitting the cab with their fists as I drive by, even if I have a fare. They're driven to the level of animals by the thought of walking home, delaying the pleasure they're promised; possible sex, more booze, greasy diner food, or well-deserved sleep. Last call is the pure lizard brain moment, the hypothalamic response to pleasure being stopped suddenly. It's fuck or fight time, and all the bars let out at once. It's pure chaos on a Roman coliseum level. Running fights down sidewalks, people puking, making out, crying collapsed on street corners. And my regular wants me to pluck him up out of the psychotic teaming multitudes. It's like landing in a hot LZ; fly in grab your man, get the hell out, and hope no one shoots at you. But he's a guaranteed forty dollar suburban trip, a good way to top the night out, so I lock the doors to my cab, and head down there, taking back streets. I tell him exactly which corner to wait on, but he's drunk and I'm not sure he'll get the right corner. I pull around the corner, dodge the hotty running frantically at me yelling and screaming, swerve around the big jock with blood on his face, and squeal up to the corner. I unlock the door and yell "get in, get in" as he and his buddies dive in. People yell at him, try to take the cab, but he yells back and says he called the damn cab, and they should fuck themselves. I begin to worry that there's going to be fight, but I get him in the cab, dodge a few other drunks and get on the highway. Whew, a close one. Man, what a clusterfuck, I think, as I gun it for suburbia.

I get them home, safe and sound, after listening to them regale each other with their failed attempts at the art of seduction. It's one forty five in the morning, and I think I can get just one more, if drive quick enough.

I head down Havana, pedal down, looking for cops, eyes a bit bleary, and almost miss my turn off onto Santa Fe. My cell rings as I'm heading around the turn off, going just a bit too fast. It's a big ass turn and I always hit it too hot. I reach frantically for my cell phone as it skitters across the seat, and hit the brakes. I'm still adrenaline amped, driving too fast, multi-tasking. I take a deep breath as I slow down and get my phone. I stop at the light and answer.

"Hello!"

"Hey, is this…the cabbie?" The voice is female and sounds out of it, spacey, not drunk, maybe stoned or tired.

"Sure is."

"You working?"

"Yep."

"It's Carrie, you picked me up the other night downtown." I draw an utter blank, I toss my card out like so many seeds in a garden, hoping some will sprout into new customers. And I give a lot of them to pretty girls.

"Yeah, sure…sure."

"Can you come and get me?" She sounds plaintive and lost, pushing all of my sucker buttons.

"Yeah, but it might be a little bit, I'm kind of south."

"No problem, I'm at 25th and Curtis, please hurry if you can."

"Give me fifteen," I say, knowing that it'll be more like twenty, twenty-five.

I hang up as the light turns green and try to crack my back as I accelerate up Santa Fe. Santa Fe runs pretty well from Havana to Mississippi and you can really haul, but you have to watch out for the drunk driving patrol at this time of night on a Friday. I keep a bleary eagle eye out for The Man at the spots where I know he'll be lurking, and get good time, barely catching the light on Mississippi. I hit the light on Alameda, and curse, tapping the steering wheel as I wait through the light, then hit everything smooth all the way through downtown, when it turns into Stout. There's a flag on Fifteenth and Stout, but I ignore him and his curses as I cruise across downtown. He was probably a decent fare, but I like to treat regulars well, especially the new ones. They're the ones that are a cabby's bread and butter on the off days. She calls me as I get stuck at a light on Nineteenth. I tell her five minutes, and wait impatiently at the light again. Nineteenth is the worst, since it has a four way pedestrian walk signal, even at two in the morning. Finally it turns and I'm free and clear until 25th, then I cut across to Curtis.

She's waiting outside of a rundown duplex, sitting on a low stone wall, knees together, feet apart, looking loose and worn out, like a punk rock rag doll. It's the girl from the porn store, the one that works in the wacker booth. Her hair is pink now, and she's wearing tattered fishnets and a tight black skirt with bondage straps, topped off with battered Doc Martins. She looks up as I stop the cab, pale eyes, with dark circles like a raccoon. For some reason I don't think it's makeup. She gets up unsteadily, shuffles to the cab, and gets in.

"Thanks," she mumbles to me, "thanks for coming, I just couldn't, couldn't…"

"Sure," I say looking for the sure signs of the puker, the green gills that give it away, as it were. She doesn't look like she's going to puke, just tired, drawn, and wan. I remember that she lives somewhere in Capitol Hill, and head that way- up to Champa, then onto Park Ave. "You going home?" I ask.

"Yeah, yeah," she mumbles, I'm beginning to think that it's not alcohol that I'm dealing with.

"Where was that again?"

"Twelfth and Marion...I'm just going to lie down back her for a bit, OK?"

"Sure honey, just no puking, OK?" Now I'm almost positive she's not drunk, probably heroin, a crying shame, just hope she doesn't OD in the back of my cab.

I get her home in record time. Lean over the seat and shake her slightly.

"Carrie...Carrie, hon, you're home." She groans slightly and swats my hand away. Fucking great.

I put on the hazards, put it in park, get out, and open the back door, squatting so I'm eye level with her passed out face. I can see the cracks in her caked on makeup and wonder what she's hiding. She's beautiful in an innocent kind of way. I shake her again, and she opens her eyes and the innocence goes away, replaced with a paranoid wariness.

"You're here, Carrie."

She seems to recognize me and smiles slightly.

"Cabbie Cowboy, how ya doin'?"

"Fine, need any help to the door?"

She seems to come to herself and sits up, adjusting bits and pieces of her outfit.

"No, no." I stand up and she gets out of the cab with a fragile dignity. I recognize it from various times I've used it myself. The posture comes from trying to maintain strict control over every aspect of your intoxicated body when it all wants to go AWOL and start thrashing about. She hands me a twenty and kisses me lightly on the cheek, she smells of jasmine and sour sweat, an odd combination.

"Thank you," she smiles sadly and wobbles up the walk into her apartment complex.

I watch her until she makes it in the door, then get in my cab and drive away. I can still feel her lips on my check, soft and tantalizing, like forbidden fruit.

✿⊙◉✿

Sometimes life just sneaks up and whacks you one. Sometimes it's out of the blue, sometimes you can almost see it coming, but the effect is the same, like a big board against the back of the skull. Wham! And you're seeing stars. That's what it was like for me, kind of a combo of both seeing it coming and out of the blue, either way it hit me like a two by four to the head.

I came home from work, eyes still feeling a bit crossed from staring at a computer monitor all day, and Mary and I started working on dinner. The kitchen was quiet with no noise but the cutting of vegetables, the simmering of water. It's a brittle silence, like neither of us wanted to say anything, almost like it's been said already and we don't want to make it worse. Then Mary's phone rang. Mary answered it.

"What?" she half choked. I stopped cutting vegetables and looked at her. She was listening, shocked, the beginning of tears glistening in her eyes. I caught her eye, questioning. She shook her head. "Ok, Ok, I'll meet you there…I'll be right down."

She hangs up and takes a big shuddering breath, then she was in my arms, crying.

"Ted's been shot, Jody's down at the hospital." The world kind of seemed to stop for a moment, out of the blue, as I said.

"How bad?" I stroked her hair, smelling the soft smell of her, thinking, almost blasphemously, that this was the first time I'd held her close in what seemed like months.

"Bad... they don't know. Jody needs me down at the hospital." She took a deep breath and stepped away, suddenly back in charge, of herself, of the situation, as much as she could be. "I'm going down there... you stay here with Mark. People will be calling, maybe stopping by, to see what's going on. I'll call you as soon as I find out, OK?" I nodded, she smiled a lopsided smile, sadness in her eyes, and kissed me on the cheek. "I love you." And then she was out the door, car keys in hand. I suddenly didn't feel much like dinner. Mechanically, I put away most of the food and made Mark his favorite dinner-mac n' cheese. Mark ate, and I put him to bed. Then sat in the living room, TV off, half drank beer in my hand, staring at the blank screen, waiting for the phone to ring.

The details came in slowly over the evening, and I passed them on to concerned friends and neighbors as the news spread. It was simple, random, and stupid. Something that happens occasionally in a big city, but never to you, never to someone you know. Someone wanted his wallet, whether he gave it to them, or whether he argued about it, it didn't matter. They shot him, once in the chest. He never really had a chance, too much damage. Mary came home around four. I was still up, trying to read a book, but I just kept reading the same paragraph over and over again, in a kind of numb shock. We went to bed, and tried to sleep, holding each other tight. I went to work in the morning, no way I couldn't, things were too shaky right then for me to take a day off. Driving to work, my mind was racing, but I felt cut off from my body, sick to my stomach, but not hungry, even if I hadn't eaten since lunch the day before.

I was a little late, and I'm sure I looked like death warmed over, so I wasn't too surprised when I got called into the manager's office. His name was John, and while we didn't really get along, we didn't not get along either. He was in his mid-forties, balding, with a slight paunch, and had a tendency to wear short-sleeved dress shirts with a tie, which, for some reason, annoyed the hell out of me. I walked into his office, and sat down wearily. He looked nervous.

"Sorry I'm late." He waved it off, and shuffled some papers around his desk, like he was looking for something to say.

"I saw in the paper there was a shooting, in Capitol Hill today, anywhere near you?" He said it lightly, just trying to find a conversation opening. I sucked in a deep breath, and tried to control my emotions.

"Yeah," I kept my response minimal, I felt fragile, about to break, "my neighbor."

He looked shocked.

"Shit, I'm sorry." I saw a flicker of guilt cross his face, and felt my gut drop lower than it was. "Makes this even harder... look, you're a good worker..." Crap, and sometimes you can almost see it coming. I nodded and walked out of the office, in even more of a daze if that was possible.

They let about half the salesmen go, with minimal severance pay, and I'm sure gave the CEO a raise or a bonus or a new car or something. I only had until the end of the week to finish things up, but I took the rest of the day off. What were they going to do, fire me?

✿◉◉✿

I wake to the noise of the neighbor's lawn mower, hot and overwhelmed by the stifling closeness of my room. Even though I didn't drink a lot the night before, I feel remarkably hung over. Disoriented, sweaty, and sore. Maybe the midgets came and beat me up while I slept for making all those jokes. I swallow and smack my lips, maybe they pooped in my mouth while they were at it. I blearily stumble to the bathroom, do my business, brush my teeth, and put on some coffee. Drinking my morning caffeine, I examine the different piles of cash I made late last night. I'm not sure what they represent, but I recognize the logic behind it: lease, mortgage, child support, bank, and a fifth pile. That's the one that mystifies me, for the life of me I can't figure out why I set that pile aside. Seat covers? Beer money? New shoes? Student loans… no, probably not. I shrug, put all the money back in one big pile and recount it. I'm stuck with my usual Saturday decision; do I pay off my entire lease, or do I set aside some of the money for the various bills? If I pay off my lease, I don't have to come into the office until Monday. On the other hand, it's nice to have some of my bills taken care of. I decide on the lease, like I usually do, count out the cash, lay a little aside for the child support, count out my bank, and head out into the afternoon.

I drive out and pay off right away and drive back to Capitol Hill. I'm feeling the lag of working so many days in a row, the repetition of driving the same streets over and over, of picking up the same people again and again. It gets to you, gets under your skin, like you're driving some sweat stained booze stinking color smeared déjà vu. I rub my eyes and swear, then drive to the next fare. It's a pick-up in Five Points, a woman, drunk at four in the afternoon, depressed and swearing, talking about her divorce. I don't want to hear about it, sympathize, give a shit, or even say a word. And I don't even have to try, she just rambles on about her asshole ex-husband, her shitty life. Freud's greatest achievement- letting all of society know that it helps, just to talk, to rant, to get it out. The recipients of this bile and ranting are supposed to be psychiatrists, churchmen, counselors, but, all too often it's bartenders, cab drivers, maybe even the person on the street. Because your friends are sick and tired of hearing about it, so I get to. At least psychiatrists go and see other psychiatrists, bartenders drink at other bars, I just get full up with other people's crap… maybe I should take more cabs, maybe that's what the notes are for, I don't know. The night goes on like a repeat of any other night, blurs into one gray mess until I'm done. I don't think I can remember one damn fare from the whole night. I park, stumble home, and fall right into bed. For once I'm too tired to count my money, tell stories, have a drink, or even jerk off. Just sleep and get the damn day over with.

❁ ◉ ◉ ❁

My sleep is filled with ghosts, hazy smoke filled streets, and a fare that I just can't find. I drive in circles, knowing it's just around the bend. The street signs are in shadow, bent and twisted. I stop the cab, get out and approach one, squinting, it is bent, with black on black letters, I can only make out the letters D and A. Shaking my head, I get back in the cab, and look in the mirror at my fare. Ted stares back at me balefully, a gaping bullet wound in his chest. I put the car in gear, and drive.

As dreams do, I find myself in front of the house that I grew up in. The rolling lawn that I hated mowing. Trim, grass short, freshly cut. I fly/float past the strawberry and rhubarb patches to the back door. The lawn stops abruptly, up against endless cornfields cut now for fall harvest, dead dry stalks lying piled up and broken at crude angles sticking up from the dun earth. There the world ends, then the fearful monsters prowl. Man eating machines and one-eyed cyclopean farmers with dusty overalls and tasseled straw hats, toting large shot guns filled with rock salt and rusty barn nails.

On to the irrigation ditches with tall cottonwoods towering over the houses, snowing down a cottony flux to fill the asphalt gutters and pile in downy drifts against the houses.

I leap the deep wide ditch in a single bound, my Superman towel/cape snapping behind me. Up the crooked boards nailed into the living wood, up and up, past tree houses simple and grand. From mere wooden platforms jammed precariously in tree branchings, to veritable Taj Mahals of weathered woods and plastic. Thousands of them, every tree house in history, I race by them, until I stand at the crown of the tree ensconced in a small bucket, swaying like a sailor in a crow's nest, thousands of miles high. I look down, the suburban neighborhood in the farm wilderness, asphalt on alfalfa. There, close to my right, is the farmhouse where the girl I fell madly in love with when I was thirteen used to live, still lived in this dream. Desperate hunts through growing fields to see my fair maiden, hiding from ogres with my hard-on in the fields. Sad, as all first loves are. I dive from the tree and became a great golden eagle. I drift over the fields, slow and lazy, then dive to land in my front yard, human again.

I walk past the old junk Chevy my dad had never fixed up, to the porch, and through the front door. The living room is empty, tan carpet new, a ragged tinsel covered Christmas tree propped in the corner. Into the kitchen I stare through the window at giant sunflowers covered in live birds and adorned with cat skulls.

Next, I creep to the basement door. I know that it leads not only to the basement, but, if you take a wrong turn on the dark twisty stairs, also to the endless tunnels under the school. There one would wander endlessly in its linoleum maze until you starved to death or the Janitaur (the bull-headed janitor, of course) found you and ate you. Then he would use your bones and hair for a new mop and squeegee.

I open the door and walked carefully down the stairs into the unfinished basement. Plastic sheets hang down, covered in dust, to the concrete floor. Blood drips into the floor drain and I follow the stream into my parent's new bedroom; the place where I lost my virginity with my sister's friend while mom and dad were out of town. Desperate coupling, frustration, and orgasm. I push aside the musty plastic and gaze upon the ruined bed. My parents are stretched out on it, mummified. My mother wears her wedding dress, holding a bouquet to her chest, arms crossed. Dad, stiff sideburns sticking out from his desiccated face, arms to his side, teeth gasping for breath, is wearing a horrible sixties tux.

✿ ◉ ◎ ✿

I wake in a cold sweat, stifling a scream. I sit up shakily and put my head in my hands. What the fuck was that? I get up, make coffee, and sit on the porch in my bathrobe. I linger over my coffee and think about taking a day off, but then I have no idea what I'd do with myself. I'd sit on the porch, drink three cups of coffee, maybe take a shower, piddle around the house putting off the inevitable trip to the bar for happy hour, where I'd get good and day drunk, come home maybe around nine at night, plastered and broke, make a sloppy dinner, and pass out in front of the TV. I try to remember when the last time I did anything constructive was. Then try to figure out what I even have to do that is "constructive".

I draw a blank, put my cowboy hat on and grab my keys. Might as well make money rather than spend it. I sit in my cab reading for about fifteen minutes until I get a call. The day goes fairly steadily and rather pointlessly. The later it gets, the more I think about my porch, beer, and the bar, even about passing out in front of the TV. The moon hangs full and heavy, large on the horizon like a white bloated tick. The streetlights blur, and my contacts feel like they're stuffed with sand, gritty and dry on my eyes. I get a call to a local bar, the bartender helps out an old man, maybe eighty, dry and wrinkled, trashed and tired. The bartender pays me, tells me the address, a few blocks away, and asks me to get him there safe. There is a tender tone of sadness in his voice that seems catching as I drive the old man the few blocks home; a retirement community right off of Colfax. I put it in park and go to help him out of the back. I open the door, and he looks at me sadly. Out of the maze of wrinkles in his face, two bright green eyes look at me. Bright green, like mine, youthful and intent. He is on the verge of tears as I hold out my hand…he speaks:

"I don't know what happened…suddenly I'm old," his voice, creaky, drunk, and old, staggers, "I didn't mean to get this old," he says, almost to himself. Then he looks at me intently, his eyes burning into mine, "I didn't mean to live this long, now, here I am, here I am." I help him up and to the door, feeling like someone punched me in the chest. I drive off, then park a block away and cry, head down on the steering wheel. I cry for age, for death, for lost youth, and for living too long.

❁◉◎❁

I spent most of that summer lying on the couch, TV off, staring at the ceiling, thinking of hanging myself in the basement. Really. Seems kind of stupid, at least to me now. But that's the thing about a heavy depression, it just drags you down into the darkness and chains you there. You can see what's happening, know that you're depressed, and that, barring the basement and the rope, you'll get over it. You can even see what an asshole you're being, but when you try to get up and motivated…nothing. Showering seems like a supreme fucking effort, eating a chore, and looking for a job a Sisyphusean endeavor akin to climbing a mountain. So, there I lay, wife bitching, child crying, collecting unemployment that just wasn't enough to pay the bills, and contemplating the cobwebs in the corners of the dark root cellar beneath me. For Mary it was interminable, the last straw in a marriage that was already on shaky ground. The end came so swift and easy, it was almost a let down. I was sitting in the kitchen, four day growth of beard, bags under my eyes, rereading the same want ad over and over, and not getting it, just not quite sure what the hell these people wanted. Pretty much the stereotypical image of the depressed out of work goon, except that I wasn't drunk.

Mary came and sat down across from me, told me that she loved me, but couldn't live like this, and that she was leaving me, going to California, and taking Mark with her. I could have the house, since I was about to lose it anyway, and that we would work out a fair settlement for child support. No screaming, no crying or flinging of dishes, no angry looks across a courtroom, neat and efficient...and cold. Mary could be like that sometimes. I nodded numbly, signed what papers needed to be signed. Then she walked out. What had taken years to build, gone in seconds. She had movers come take her stuff, while I sat there, numb and watched the house empty of her things, her smell, her touch. By the end of the week, I was sitting in the dark in an empty house wondering what the fuck had happened. That's the closest I've been to the noose. I think what saved me was Mark, I just couldn't think of him growing up the son of a suicide. So, instead of killing myself, I showered, shaved, put on clean clothes, and got a job, the first one that came up. Several months and maybe a lifetime too late.

Burn the Eyes from the Bobble-Headed St. Christopher on my Dashboard

Saint Christopher is missing...
Maybe he's lost
Or kidnapped
bound and blindfolded in my glove box
Lost and dizzy-headed
From suburban turns
Circles
And courts
Tried by greengrass juries
And lawn ornament covenants
Executed for sedition
For painting his house the wrong color
Perhaps an army of fat men
Wearing "kiss the cook" aprons and bar-b-que tongs
Laid him out
On a rack
Made of lost car keys
And broken turn signals
Branded him with red hot hubcaps
and whipped him with gleaming steel antennae
Or maybe,
Just maybe
the old guy just went out for a beer
At some rundown roadhouse
at the edge of the desert
And he sits there still
Sipping his drink
Covered in the dust of the road
Replaced by mapquest
Weary
And sick of it all
Either way,
I drive in suburban circles
Past empty lawns for Nintendo children
And houses with neighborhood watch windows
And wonder where the fuck I am

PART 2

Monday rolls around, hot and bleak, like the bleached bones of the day, the picked over carcass of the weekend, scattered in a dirty lion's den. I crawl out of bed, bones creaking, knee weak and pissy from staying in the same position for hours. I check the mail, throwing out the junk mail and cursing silently at the overdue electric bill, threatening shut off of services. I have until Friday to pay off the overdue balance. I should be able to pay it, and everything else off, if I take no days off, I try to figure when the last day off I had was, and figure I've been working for ten days straight and will have to work another six at least.

Not that I have anything else really pressing to do. I think that the fact that I have nothing to do if I took a day off bothers me more than the idea of working 16 days in a row. Money. The crunch and crinkle of money seems to be on my brain all the time. I guess it's that way when you don't have enough, although I can't think of a time when I've had enough.

Even when I was making 50k a year, money problems were always there, make more money spend more money. I've never lived any other way than paycheck to paycheck, dollar to dollar, always behind, always worried. It's the providence of the middle class, the nightmare of the lower. The concept of investment seems ludicrous to me, just like the concept of "spare" money. I make a quick run to the ATM, these thoughts buzzing in my head, and deposit my "extra" money in the bank, write out what checks I can, and mail them off. Child support covered, late mortgage payment almost covered, student loans long gone into default. Long ago I made the not so difficult choice of keeping my house or paying my student loans. Last time I checked, with penalties and interest, I owed them over a hundred thousand on a forty thousand dollar loan. They stick a shoplifter in jail, but bankers get cabinet level posts, you figure it out. I walk over to the post office and mail the bills. Walking along, I realize that I'm wheezing a little bit. I guess the walk to the bank is about all the exercise I get these days. Great. On top of taking up all of my time, the job is making me fat and out of shape. For about the fifth time this week I think that I'm too young to feel this old. The gym. That's it, I'll join a gym…next time I have some "spare" time and money. What a fucking joke. I walk (mentally waddling) back to my house, sweating a bit in the afternoon sun, hop in my cab, log in, and head out to a fine Monday behind the motor.

❀ ◉ ◎ ❀

There are some beautiful nights driving a cab; the new moon, Cheshire Cat full, grinning below a bright Venus, like the night is fucking winking at me. My pockets jammed full of cash, hurtling through the night from one fare to another. The lights are all green and I feel the joy of driving, just driving, like when I was kid with a new car, taking it out on the back roads near Longmont and just seeing how fast it would go. Cruising down York street, hugging the curves, feeling the power of the police interceptor beneath me, not worried about cops, or money, or bills, just living the moment. Nights full of short skirts and promises, happy customers, huge tips, and hassle free rides. Those are the good nights.

Then there are the bad nights; broke, doling out five bucks at a time into the gas tank, sweating blood over bills, short fares, and ugly fares bitching like I stole the family fortune when I went around the block rather than make an illegal U-turn. Ghetto fares arguing over fifteen cents, or where my fares have drank themselves to the level of three year olds: "poo"… "Yer funny, he, he". Ripped off by some young gangster kid running on a forty dollar fare to some fucking ghetto project maze in fucking Aurora. A night when you hate the poor with their cheapness, their avarice, a night when you hate the rich just as much for their condescension, the way they flaunt their wealth and women. Nights full of hate and headaches, mayhem and murder. Where the roads are full of drunks and bad drivers, where horrible twisted wrecks of cars block the streets, and cops are everywhere.

And most nights it's a mixture of the two.

❀◉◎◉❀

I'm downtown in Lodo, pure yuppie hell, chock full of the kind of people I grew up hating, and now where I make most of my money. I do a drop at a restaurant, and cruise the Market Street corridor between Fourteenth and Seventeenth with what seems like every cab in Denver, I turn up Seventeenth, turn down Larimer caught in the flow of cabs. Most turn down 15th to do the same endless route until they pick up a fare, like sharks circling for chum. I keep going on Larimer, decide to get the hell out of downtown and wait on Capitol Hill for a bell off the board rather than waste the gas on driving around downtown with a hundred other sad sacks. I turn up Fourteenth and I'm about to hit the gas so I can make the poorly timed lights out of downtown, when I see a hand wave frantically out of the corner of my eye. I quickly pull over to the curb, and look in the mirror to see if I stopped in time. I see a group of four, two women and two men, being led by a small pretty Asian woman. The rest look vaguely Middle Eastern, but Americanized, if you get my drift. I start moving my passenger seat detritus: clip board, credit card "knuckle buster", water bottle, book, etc. I move these back and forth between the passenger seat and the area between the two front seats at least four times a night. The passenger seat is easier access, and the stuff tends to stay there rather than slip and slide into the back seat to rattle around at my passengers' feet.

When I look back up the woman has reached us, while the two men and the other woman are arguing. The Asian women gets in the back and gives me an address, and I overhear part of the argument.

"Why did she give him her phone number?" One man is shouting. I can't hear the woman's response. I'm waiting for the Asian woman to close the door, so I can take off, I have a feeling that this is going to turn ugly, and I want to grab my fare and get the hell out of there. I look in the mirror and my fare seems distraught. I'm stuck with indecision, not sure of what I should do. The man makes a break around the woman and leaps into the back of the cab. He grabs her and yells.

"You are prostitute, whore!" He turns to me. "You drive, just drive and nothing will happen."

I don't know if this is a threat to me or to her, but I feel my blood boil, and I see red. I slam it into park and reach for my seatbelt. I'm ready to beat this guy's face into the hood of my cab until he bleeds.

"Get the fuck out of my cab!" I yell. This puts a pause on him, like he's stunned a mere menial like myself would talk like that. I undo my seat belt and reach for the door. He moves quick and gets out of the cab.

"Fine, whore! I move my things out," he yells as the other woman gets in and shuts the door.

"Please drive," the other woman says quietly.

"Prostitute!" The man yells as I drive away, one woman consoling the other n woman in a foreign language that sounds like Japanese spoken with an Arabic accent, the other quietly sobbing.

I refasten my seatbelt at a stoplight and I am not surprised to find that my hands are shaking.

My next fare is a good long fare, an interesting drunk who keeps telling me jokes that are actually funny. He tips me well, and I give him may card, things are balancing out a bit.

Carrie calls me later, needs a ride. She sounds upbeat, a contrast to Friday night. I drive out to York and 40th to pick her up in a maze of warehouses. Dim brick monstrosities made sinister by moonlight.

She guides me in by cell phone, and I know I'm close by the noise: chatter and electronic thumping.

She's waiting outside the party, leaning up against the tan bricks, one leg cocked up, smoking, neon pink fishnets flashing in the dark, short skirt showing lots of leg, thighs slightly dimpled by the elastic of the garters. She waves and skips up to the car, a little knock-kneed with heavy stomper boots. She exhales smoke and flicks the cigarette into the darkness, an arc of red, then a firework splash as it hits the asphalt of the parking lot.

She leans in, smiling, and tugs the brim of my cowboy hat. Her eyes a bright and glassy, she seems flushed, vibrant, full of energy.

"Howdy, cowboy," she grins, I see that her lower front teeth are a bit crooked. Her top is a loose cut up t-shirt with the woman from Fritz Lang's Metropolis on the front. As she leans in, the cut off neck billows down and I can see the soft curve of her breasts, small, pert, with no bra. I try not to look while still looking. Quite a quandary.

"Can I ride up front?" she bubbles.

"Uh, sure," I mumble and go through the resorting routine again. She walks around the front of the cab, pops in a piece of gum, and slides into the passenger's seat.

"Home?" I ask.

"Yep," she replies, reaching between her legs and scooting the seat back.

We drive in silence for a while, just the sound of the road, the murmur of the radio, and her gum popping, the she asks me to turn up the radio. She jerks her head in time to the music, leans her seat back, staring into the night. We drive down Thirteenth Street, and, as I'm about to turn onto Marion, she asks me to go up the alley. I shrug and do as ordered. We pull in behind her apartment building, I put the cab in park, and turn down the radio.

"Let's see... looks like twelve fifty." She looks at me slyly and leans in, I catch that whiff of jasmine again.

"Look, I don't have any cash, how 'bout a blowjob?"

My mind skitters to a stop. I almost automatically say no, but hesitate, I haven't been with a woman in over a year. I feel a stab of heat in my groin, as my body answers my mind's question. She smiles broader and winks at me, all bright eyes and teeth.

"Of course you do. Now, turn off the car and undo your pants."

Breathing a little heavy, I turn off the car and the lights, undo my belt and the buttons on my jeans. Her hand darts into my pants almost before I'm done unbuttoning. She pulls out my penis, already hard. I suck in my breath as she touches me. With her other hand, she fishes out her gum and hands it to me.

"Here, hold this."

Feeling like a dumb spectator in my own life, I numbly take the gum in my left hand. Her head dives down almost as soon as I take the gum and she suddenly engulfs me. I moan involuntarily as her warm wet mouth wraps around my cock.

She grabs me firmly with one hand while snaking her other hand under her skirt. She writhes and moans as she goes down on me and the combination of the sucking and moaning noises drive me crazy.

I'm worried that someone will see us and I'm caught between losing myself in the sensation and keeping an eye out for the cops, which somehow heightens the excitement.

Bits of the dim street lit scene hit me as I begin climbing. The tattoo of a Chinese character at the nape of her neck, right where the hair fades from pink to mousy brown. Her hips grinding against her hand. The yellow of the streetlight on her bare thigh between her hiked up skirt and the edge of her fishnets. My hand resting on the small of her back, part of her t-shirt in my clenched fist, as my hips thrust up, driving myself into her throat. And, abstractly, as an almost absurd counter-point to the whole thing, my left arm, elbow resting on the door handle, forearm straight up, thumb and index finger daintily holding a wad of half chewed bright pink bubble gum.

Suddenly I peak and come, like a rocket, like bright lights, like a fucking farmhouse dropping on a prairie road. Use whatever metaphor you want, I am drained and gasping as she sits up, smacks her lips and takes the piece of gum from my trembling hand.

"You taste good," she said. I almost laugh, that being a pure lie, I'm sure I taste like sweat, cheap beer, and failure. "I'm broke, can I have ten bucks for that?"

"Sure," I mumble, brain all a bits, post-coital retardation setting in, and hand her a ten spot.

"Thanks," she leans in and kisses me on the cheek, "you're sweet. See you around." She opens the door and walks off quietly, hips swaying.

I sit there for a moment, fly open, moist limp dick staring at me in accusation.

"Shut up," I tell it, button up my pants and drive off. I realize that I had just paid for sex for the first time in my life. I feel confused and dirty and a little elated all at the same time.

I drive a few more bells in a daze, absentmindedly scratching a dick made itchy by drying saliva and semen, then call it a night.

I get home and pour myself a glass of scotch. I sip and try to put some sort of order and sense into my evening. I fail miserably. Sipping the scotch, my eye catches my dusty guitar propped up in the corner. I set the scotch aside, go grab a cleanish sock, and wipe the dust gently from the neck, strings, and body of the guitar. It's a beat up old Hagstrom, not much of a guitar, but I always liked it. I play a chord and wince. Even not plugged in, it is painfully out of tune, not that I expect anything else. I set it back on its stand, and go to the kitchen to root through the junk drawer to see if my tuner is in there.

I dig through the detritus of the junk drawer: screwdrivers, light switches, Christmas bulbs, a tampon… a tampon? I idly hold up the tampon, a strange reminder of living with a woman, which seems to represent my life and my divorce. She took random things when she left. Took all of the cookware but left all of the silverware. Took all of the bedding and towels, but left the bed, like she didn't want to buy new sheets, but couldn't stand to sleep on the bed where we conceived Mark.

I remember standing, confused, in some giant Meglomart of a department store, looking at a seemingly endless aisle of sheets, comforters, and pillowcases. Almost all of them were pastels; yellows, eggshell blues, pinks. I stood there and wondered who decorated their bedrooms like fucking Easter eggs for a few solid minutes, shoppers wheeling their carts around me, catching the occasional odd glance. Portrait of the frozen bachelor. Mary had always done this sort of thing, not really a his/her husband/wife division of labor thing, just more that I didn't give a crap. If had been up to me we would have been still sleeping on a futon on the floor with crusty mismatched sheets and lumpy pillows. Finally I walked down the horrendous pastel shit-storm of an aisle, poking at random packages, not even sure of the size of my bed, hoping to find something that didn't look like the Easter Bunny puked on it. I grabbed the first dark set of sheets, a blue blanket, and some pillowcases, and half ran from the place. The sheets were too big, but I just folded them under.

So, for some reason, this tampon brings all that back to me. Like this tube of cotton and paper strikes home all that is fucked up and miserable in my life. I twiddle it between my fingers, bemused, then toss it in the general direction of the trashcan. Fuck it, where's my goddamn tuner? After digging a bit more, I find it and a spare battery and go into the living room to tune the guitar. As I fiddle with some bar chords, some lyrics come to me:

She's a series of missed opportunities
A bundle of neuroses and lunacy
She's a mess of dichotomies
Her smile hits me just like a lobotomy
She's a woman made up of contradictions
Broken hearts and terrified addictions
But she's so hot that she burns me
One long look and she turns me

I strum one more chord and stop. Great. I think I'm falling for a twenty-year-old junkie who works in a wacker booth and gives out ten-dollar blowjobs. Perfect. I'm fucked, I think, as I set my guitar back on its dusty perch, and head to my room for some much needed sleep.

❀◉◉◉❀

Accidents happen. If you drive sixty hours or more a week, week after week, something is going to happen, you just hope it isn't your fault.

There was the time in the middle of winter, black ice streets, blowing winds, a Saturday night. The board was lit up, my regulars calling me incessantly. Run the meter, book in, get a fare, a night to make a small fortune. One problem, though; the streets were slick. Cars sliding around like hockey pucks, assholes in four wheel drive vehicles burning by at forty, then slamming into parked cars when they realized that four-wheel drive doesn't mean four-wheel stop. Even going ten miles an hour you could end up on someone's front lawn, peeking shame faced from your car and apologizing for parking on their hedges. It was the kind of night where no one should be out driving, yet you have to make some money.

My tires were bald, and my cab had become nothing better than a rear-wheel driven two-ton sled. I was parked at a squirrel-run light. One of those pointless lights on 13th Street, that seem to have no reason to exist except to let the squirrels cross. The light changes, and I press the gas, feel the tires spin, and stay motionless at the light. I look in the mirror and see traffic coming, and realize I'm a sitting duck. I pump the breaks so my brake lights flash, hit the gas again, and see the car behind me coming. A Jeep, going way too fast, probably talking on their cell phone.

To me it happens in slow motion. My tires spinning, the lights getting closer, the eerie skating of the car behind me, almost floating, then the inevitable crunch of the car slamming into my bumper, my cab finally fucking moving as I drift/slide into a loading zone in front of an old folks home, then up on the curb. I'm shaken and pissed, and have to restrain myself from hopping out of the cab and slapping the living shit out of the dumbfuck behind me. Instead, I do a quick self-check, realize I'm fine, except for a stiff neck, get out of the car, make sure the driver is OK. She is OK, just mildly hysterical. Then I call dispatch, and tell them I've been in a wreck, the fourteenth of the night apparently.

After that, it's just a nice long wait for the police and our company's accident investigator. I sit in my cab, occasionally turning it on to stay warm, ticking off the minutes and dollars I'm losing, telling my regulars as they call that they are on their own. The cop rules in my favor, it's obviously not my fault. Then I have to drive back to motor, fill out a form, sign it, then try to get a cab ride back to my place. No more driving for me until a review with a manager and a once over of my cab by a mechanic. An impromptu night off, although the manager will only see you at eight in the morning, which is a solid punch in the nuts for a night driver. If you're lucky this doesn't happen to you on a Friday, because the manager only works weekdays, which seems stupid since cab driving is a 24/7 kind of industry. As I said, accidents are inevitable, and you just hope that they aren't bad, and pray that they aren't your fault.

❀ ◉ ◎ ◉ ❀

I wake up, eyes gummed shut, sheets tangled around me like rope. It's like swimming up from a deep depth, and when I finally surface, I lie there trying to remember what I was dreaming about, but only recall fragments of turning wheels, bright smiles, and green grass for some reason. I lie there for at least ten minutes, then drag myself up and into the shower.

I stand in the shower, leaning my head against the cool tiles, trying to make some sense of the night before, and fail miserably. I get dressed and head straight out on the road. I'm not sure if I'll work all day, or just until the company turns me off. A beer sounds like pure elixir, and I imagine myself sitting on a patio somewhere getting good and day drunk. Sun beating down on me, beer in my hand, or maybe a nice ice cold margarita, water beading on the side of the glass. It's pure torture, since I know that once I get going I won't stop, just drive, trying to tick off the bills as they're paid off.

It's a weekday, so I sit in my cab and read a book for a good half an hour before I get a call. A voucher, pick up at the Mental Health Center in Capitol Hill, drop near DU. A good fare, even with the 10% voucher fee taken out. I pull in, call the contact number, get the switchboard for MHC, and hang up, wondering who the fuck doesn't have a cell phone in this day in age. I start to punch in a no job, bitching to myself about people who don't leave a reliable number and aren't waiting right the fuck there. I'm about to drive off when she comes out waiving frantically. I wave back and nod, turn on the meter and start filling out the voucher form, as she walks up. She opens the rear passenger door and stops. I sit there waiting for her to get in, and she doesn't. I look over my shoulder and see her frozen with the door open, looking at the seat. Fucking great.

"How ya doing?" I ask in my best friendly cab driver voice. She pulls her eyes away from the back seat with an effort, and meets my eyes with a hesitant smile.

"It's filthy back here."

I sigh deeply and try to keep my temper. "Ma'am I just vacuumed and washed it." I know what's bothering her, I have cloth seats and there's a lot of wear and tear on them, and the last thing I want to spend my money on is a steam vac. They look grungy, I'll admit that, but just as bad as any other cab.

"But... It's filthy." Crap, I've got a neat freak, of course, it's probably pathological considering I picked her up at MHC.

"Car has three hundred thousand miles on it, ma'am, I do the best I can." She hesitates, I can see she's trying to be sympathetic, but failing.

"You should ask for another cab."

"I'm on the list for a new one," I lie. There is no fucking list. If I want a better cab, I can turn mine in and wait, hope a better one comes open. Fat chance, I'm stuck with this one. She nods and says she'll be right back. She runs/waddles into the building, opening the door with a napkin. I sigh and finish filling out the paperwork. Great way to start the fucking day off. She comes back, carrying a newspaper, spreads it over the seat and floor and gets in.

"Sorry," she says nervously, "I should carry some plastic with me, these cabs are so dirty." She shivers, and I actually feel sorry for her.

"No problem." I drive out of the parking lot and head up to York to get across town. The ride is a quiet one, with her huddled into herself, doing her best to avoid touching anything in the cab. We pull up to her apartment building, and I hand her the voucher to sign. She takes the clipboard with two fingers, and grabs the pen like it's a snake, quickly signs, then hands them back to me. I can tell she wants to wipe her hands on something, but everything is too dirty. I wonder briefly what it's like living where common objects are the enemy, where you are terrified of common dirt, washing your hands fifty times a day. Considering the amount of money I touch, I should probably have the same feelings. I consider getting some hand sanitizer for the cab. She gets out and looks at the newspapers forlornly. I smile and tell her I will take care of them. She flutters another nervous smile, looking relieved, thanks me and shuts the door. I book back in, drive to the nearest gas station, and throw out all the papers. Earning a dirty look from the counter person when I don't buy any gas.

I'm on Buchtel, about to make a right onto University when she rides in front of me. I'm distracted and don't recheck as I make the turn. She's barreling through the intersection, and I barely stop in time. Her bike hits my bumper and she flies ass over teakettle. I put it in park, all the time repeating a mantra of: shit, shit, shit, shit. I get out to see if she's OK and stop in my tracks. Sitting on the curb, nursing a skinned knee is Jody. She looks up, eyes filled with fear, stares at me for a moment, then her eyes light up as she recognizes me.

"Hey."

"Hey yourself," I crouch down next to her, "you OK?"

"Skinned my knee is all," she puts her arm on my shoulder and stands up. I walk over to her bike, the front rim is bent.

"Looks like I have to get your bike fixed for you," I half joke, "where you headed?"

"Um, downtown."

"Well, we'll pop your bike in the trunk, stop by my place and we'll fix up that knee, then I'll drop you downtown, all right?"

"Uh, sure," she still looks terrified and unsure. I put my hand on her arm and gently turn her towards me.

"You sure you're OK?" I ask. She looks up from the corner and stares me in the eye.

"Yeah, it's just that…"

"What?" I ask, concerned.

"It's just that, " her hand tightens on my arm, "I saw him, I swear I saw Ted, right before you hit me, that's why I wasn't looking."

I say nothing, feeling the skin on my arms crinkle and stand up. I say nothing, although I know I should. I say nothing, because the reason I was distracted, is that I thought I saw him too.

✿◉☉✿

We drive in silence, my trunk popping up and down behind me, probably crunching her beat up bike even more. My hands are still shaking, post adrenaline wreck nerves with an addition of the fucking heebie jeebies. I'm an extremely rational chap, not given to flights of fancy or Ghost Hunter marathons, and probably I'd have put it off to too much coffee, mistaken identity, or swamp gas reflecting the light of Venus if she hadn't seen something too. I try to put it out of my mind as we pull up in front of my house. Jody seems dazed and a little fearful as she looks at my house, and her old house looking strangely empty next to mine. I realize that I haven't even tried to meet the new neighbors. I must seem like some strange night dwelling hermit to them. I get out and open the door for Jody and help her out.

"Joseph, you don't have to-"

"Of course I do," I cut her off, "I've got some band aids and stuff inside, won't take long." She smiles and nods.

"OK, but I can walk on my own."

"Sure, let me get your bike." I get her bike, throw it awkwardly over my shoulder, haul it up to the porch, and open the door. She walks in and sits on the couch.

"Not much different," she says, studiously ignoring how filthy it is.

"No," I reply, suddenly nervous, wishing I had actually picked up at some point. "Mary didn't take much when she left."

She looks down, I stand there for a moment, realizing I just entered uncomfortable space, then head upstairs to the bathroom and grab some cotton balls, hydrogen peroxide, antibiotic ointment, a box of band aides, and a wad bandages. Probably overkill, but I have them, I might as well use them. When I come downstairs she's sitting awkwardly on the couch, hands between her knees. I set my impromptu first aid kit down on the coffee table and kneel down in front of her.

"You still play?" She points to the guitar in the corner.

"Not so much," I chuckle as I pour some hydrogen peroxide on a few cotton balls, "in fact last night was the first time in almost a year." First time in a year for a few things, a snickering voice comments in my head. I dab her skinned knee and she winces, drawing in a quick breath.

"Ow."

"Sorry, doing the best I can."

"I know," she smiles and looks around obviously casting about for something to say, obviously avoid certain subjects. There's a whole range of things floating in the air that neither one of us wants to talk about. "It's a good thing you have a full med kit floating about," she jokes, pointing at the medical supplies arrayed on the coffee table.

"Had to have them around when Mark was here," she looks away again. Great, I'm king of the uncomfortable moment apparently. I quickly finish cleaning the scrapes, then grab the tube of ointment. I'm suddenly aware of her smell, a clean smell, with a hint of girl sweat. The uncomfortable moment stretches, then I know that I've got to say something, anything, to rescue the conversation.

"So, ah, what're you up to these days," I ask, hoping that this avenue of conversation doesn't drift down uncomfortable moment lane.

"Working downtown, living up near DU," she smiles, obviously relieved at a hopefully emotional minefield free line of conversation.

"You like it?" I ask as I start rubbing the ointment into her knee carefully. She shifts her leg and lifts up her knee. I'm very conscious of the feel of her calf in my hand, the curve of her knee, the taught muscles of her thighs, and of me kneeling in front of her almost in supplication. I clear my throat and quickly let go of her leg as I grab the band-aides and start opening them. Her response is lost as I run a quick inner dialogue of self-condemnation, wonder what the hell I'm thinking as I try to mentally chase away the stirrings of an erection. What the hell am I thinking? Didn't the bj from the night before do anything? Apparently nothing but clear the horny cobwebs from my libido. Goodbye chronic masturbator, hello chronic leg humper.

"... don't you think?' She finishes the sentence and I'm at a loss as to what the hell she just said.

"Um, sure, sure," smooth. I quickly slap the band-aides on in a sloppy and haphazard manner, then stand up. "There you go, Jody, almost as good as new."

I go to the kitchen to wash my hands, which are still shaking a bit, then come back into the living room drying my hands.

"Guess we should get you downtown."

We head back to my cab and drive downtown.

"You going to need a ride back?"

"No, she says, looking out the window, I'll take the light rail."

The rest of the trip is silent, and I drop her off in front of an office building. I get her number and tell her I'll be in touch about her bike. I'm about to drive off when she leans back in to the cab.

"It was good to see you," she smiles shyly, "even under the circumstances.

"Yeah, it was," I reply and realize that it actually was. I promise again to call her, then drive away, still smelling the confusing scent of her perfume and cheap antibiotic ointment. When life is ordinary, life is boring, when it's interesting, it's complicated.

❀ ◉ ◎ ❀

Robbery, murder, and mayhem. They're always sitting in the back of your mind like an angry troll. Especially late late at night, when the streets are empty and the accidents are piled up, all twisted wreckage and blood, flashing lights and fire. Cabs don't have the glass in Denver, just an open car and the possibility of a bullet in the back of the head. It's a safe city, overall, but there's still the possibility of some asshole that needs another fix and has a gun or a knife. I figure if it comes to that I can always drive the cab into a building, most of my passengers don't wear seatbelts anyway.

Don't get me wrong, just because I don't pack a gun doesn't mean that I don't take measures. In bad neighborhoods I don't drive down alleys. I leave the car in drive in case I want to make the afore-mentioned wild ride into the side of building, I hide my money in various spots around my body. Sometimes, I stop at home and dump a hundred or so, just so I'm not holding more than eighty bucks. I think of weapons, mace (bad, bad idea in an enclosed space like a cab), run scenarios in my head, wonder how good a pen jabbed into someone's knee cap would work. In the downtimes you think of it, wonder about it.

When it's busy you don't think about it until that guy gets in the cab. The jumpy twitchy type, all blood shot eyes and desperation, not giving you an address, just badly defined directions. He gets in the cab right behind the driver's seat and you feel his hot breath on your neck, the hairs stands up on your body, and you start looking for convenient telephone poles to drive into. Then it ends up being nothing, just late night paranoia, and maybe even a good tip...so far, anyway.

❀◉◎◉❀

Something about seeing Jody drives me to ignore the thoughts of a beer on the patio, and throw myself into work with gusto. Maybe frustrated sexual energy, maybe just the fact that I told her I would fix her bike, adding another bill to the monumental bill pile. I work past last call, picking up a good fare that takes me from downtown all the way out deep into Aurora. I'm even more tired than usual, but my hands seem to move on their own, booking me in, and accepting the call automatically. Luckily, it's fairly easy to find since I don't know Aurora very well. I find it, and pull into one of the endless apartment complexes that ring the city like broken teeth. I drive through the pools of dim yellow streetlight trying to find the building in a suburban ghetto maze.

I find it, make the call and wait, rubbing my eyes and stretching my legs. It's past three in the morning, and I swear this is my last fare. I see him coming, a big guy, shaved head, vaguely Hispanic, tattooed old English letters on his neck. A straight up gangbanger as far as I can see. Great, just fucking great. I figure how much money I have and curse slightly: over two hundred. He gets in the front seat, and I move my stuff, feeling slightly more nervous. That never makes me feel good, when they jump in the front. I smell the sharp tang of booze and weed, and don't know whether to be relieved and more nervous. He gives me an address, and I drive off. I don't tell him to fasten his seat belt just in case I have to launch him through the windshield. A shitty attitude, but I'm tired and nervous and don't feel charitable or PC.

"So," he asks slightly slurred, hunched down in his seat, "you been working all night?"

Could be friendly banter, could be feeling me out to see if I have any money. I feel the dark wings of paranoia fluttering, and the troll in the back of my mind starts grumbling and looking around for a rock. I gun the engine as we get on the highway, his fingers clutch convulsively on the dashboard, and he quickly puts on his seat belt. So much for that idea.

"No, just started," I lie, "work the end of the bar rush and on through the morning."

"Must be a bitch, those hours."

"Nah, I'd be up anyway, I'm a night person, insomnia." That's true enough.

"You like this job, good money?"

"It's all right, pay the cab company most of my money."

He grunts and we ride for a while in silence, I pull off of 225 and onto Mississippi.

"Pretty dangerous job, don't you ever get worried about getting robbed?" Shit. I feel my balls try to crawl into my torso, and my cock shrivel up.

"Nah, I used to bounce at some pretty scary bars," I say steadily and turn to look him in the eye, "I can handle myself pretty well." No threat, just a statement, and luckily my voice stays steady and doesn't warble and give away the fact that I'm scared as shit. He's a pretty big guy, and I wonder if I can grab my pen and jam it into his eye before he stabs or shoots me or whatever. He nods, looks back forward and grins.

"Cool... turn here." We pull in front of a well-kept house, with a nice yard, and a few late model cars in front. He gets out and tosses me a twenty.

"Keep it man, stay safe." He saunters into the house, and I let out an explosive breath that I didn't know I'd been holding. Fuck. You never really know, do you? Enough of this shit, I think, it's time to call it a night. I head back out, taking Mississippi into town.

❁ ◉ ◉ ❁

Some nights just don't end. I just keep taking one more ride, then one more fucking ride like some kind of gasoline fueled zombie. It's a spastic kind of reflex, the hand comes up, and my foot hits the brake. I've passed clean through exhaustion and I'm in some kind of fugue state where I could drive for fucking ever until I fell off the edge of the earth. Sometimes it's the money that's driving me. Too little or so much I can't stop, either way there's more to make, more miles to drive, more people to pick up. I think my record is eighteen hours behind the wheel. I didn't feel like I was driving anymore, just a floating rubber doll behind the wheel, terrible and dangerous. But I kept going, slamming down the coffee, until my gut hurt and my fingers twitched. That's the beauty and danger of driving a cab, if you need more money, really need it, then you can just conceivably drive more and more until you get it, eighteen hours, twenty hours, maybe a nap in your cab, and go, go, go. There used to be a check in the computer system to cut you off after sixteen hours, eighty in a week. It would book you out automatically, but you could still pick up flags if you timed it right. I used to book out around bar rush on purpose so I could put in more hours over the week. Then they put in the new system, and somehow conveniently forgot to include that feature in the upgrade. Now you can drive till you drop... or drive off the road. Good for the cabbies, not so good for the general public.

❁ ◉ ◉ ❁

I'm two blocks from my house when I see the two guys with the bike frantically waiving me down. I find myself pulling over before I even consciously think about it, and start cursing under my breath.

Why the fuck did I pull over? I just want to be home and in bed by now, I don't even really want a drink for once. I'm just thinking of my head hitting that pillow, dirty sheets pulled around me, and a dark dark room without flashing headlights and noisy passengers.

The two guys run up to the car, one leans in the back, a short guy with kind of wild eyes, and a scrubby beard, pupils dilated; obviously fucked up on something.

"Can you open the trunk?" He says breathlessly.

I pop the trunk and watch for a moment as they wrestle with the bike for a bit, trying to get the bike in the trunk. I sigh and get out, knees popping, and look back at them, leaning on the top of my cab.

"Look, guys, I'm not going to drive with the trunk open," I say. I've done it before, but I'm looking for any excuse to get out of this last fare and get to bed.

"OK," says the other guy, a wiry little guy in basketball shorts, a long flannel, and a baseball cap set at an angle on his head. He shrugs and tosses the bike into the lawn of the house I'm pulled over in front of. "Let's go," he grins a manic grin and gets in the back. What the fuck, I get back in the cab. They ask me to take them to a place in the Highlands and I head down 13th to Speer up and over I-25. They're both kind of twitchy, whispering and giggling.

They have me turn up 34th and ask me to turn up an alley. It's a fairly well lit alley, so, although I'm not too happy about it, I turn into it. They have me stop about halfway up behind a ramshackle garage with splintery faded blue doors that have seen better times. I leave the cab in drive, just in case. The ride is $12.60. The short wild eyed guy gets out and says he'll be right back with the cash. I look back to make sure that the wigger looking guy is staying in the cab. He grins, and I see the handles of a pair of bolt cutters sticking out of his flannel. That explains why he was so cavalier with the bike, and in such a hurry to get out of there. The short guy disappears into the garage, and a few moments later a bizarre apparition walks out. He is ghostly white, with disheveled hair about two months gone from a decent haircut. He is shirtless, barefoot, and skinny with ribs show-ing through milky skin.

As he walks up to my window, I see that his fly is undone. His rainbow hued boxer shorts stick out the zipper. He is wearing one rubber glove. He reaches into his wallet and pulls out a twenty with his latex covered digits and hands it to me daintily between two fingers. I take it between two fingers as well, like its radioactive or covered in Vaseline, which, in this case, it could be. The wigger gets out giggling, and ghost boy nods to me.

"Keep it."

You got it, weirdo. I drive out of that alley, still holding the twen-ty, then set it down carefully on the seat, not sure if I want to touch it. For a moment I try to imagine what the hell was going on back in that garage, then decide that I don't want to know. On my way home, a man that I swear was in an evening gown tries to flag me down on Speer. I keep driving, eyes forward until I get home and to bed.

❀ ◉ ◎ ❀

The next day I get up bright and early- around noon. I sit, bleary eyed on my front porch in my bathrobe, coffee in hand. When I woke up my eyes were swollen shut and it took a bit of effort to pry one open, the eyelashes laced together with dried eye snot. Sipping my coffee I work on my eyelashes, getting the cement and gravel off of them.

I go inside for another cup of coffee and see Jody's bike leaned up against my bookcase. I set my coffee down on the porch, come back inside and wheel the bike out, front tire wobbling, chain hanging loose. Looks like I fucked it up pretty good. Squinting in the early afternoon sunshine, I sit and wheel it back and forth thinking about Jody, and Mary, and inevitably Ted.

It's strange how people float in and out of your life. Sometimes they just fade away and you find yourself reminded of them years down the road by a fragment of a song, or the way the wind blows, a wisp of perfume, or even a stranger's laugh. You kind of stop and wonder what the fuck happened to them. And then sometimes, they just pop right back into your life, become important again, sometimes more important than before... Makes you wonder if it's all random or if there is such a thing as fate, makes you wonder about all of the people that might as well be extras in your life. Will they return and be something more, or do they exist in more or less a peripheral way that doesn't really matter in the long run, just bits of background scenery?

I roll the bike back and forth on the porch watching the wheel wobble, and think about Jody's calf in my hand, muscular and smooth, and am somehow filled with a deep sadness for life, mean-ingless life. How we aren't attached or close as we need to be, how we're all alone in our heads, and can never really reach each other. I let the bike fall against the railing and get up, suddenly irritated at myself. I tell myself I'll fix the damn thing tomorrow. I head inside, get changed, and head out for day twelve on the road.

It's a weekday, and, thus, slow as hell. I pick up a few fares but spend most of my time in the cab reading. Then the night starts sliding downhill. I do a pick-up in Five Points, a run to the Grey-hound station. Bus trips are kind of a letdown. You see them walk up, pulling luggage, and start thinking that the day won't be a total wash. A ride to the airport is $45 plus tip, minimum. Even one run pops your night right up. You've got half your pay out right there and can relax. So, you get out of the cab, joints creaking, and put on your best "I'm here to serve" smile, pop the trunk and help load their luggage. Then they tell you "bus station please." Like I've said, every ride is a roll of the dice, and you just crapped out. A seven dollar fare instead, and most likely a shitty tip. I mean they're taking the bus, so you know they're broke, right? Still I try to put on a good happy face, be friendly. Who knows, they maybe a big tipper who's afraid of flying.

So I do the luggage monkey thing, and the couple gets in. No smiles, general grunts to any conversation, a nice grumpy fare. Then they start arguing. I turn the radio up, and do my best not to pay attention, hoping that they won't try to pull me in.

It's happened before, my fares trying to pull me into the argument on one side or another. I usually just try to give the most noncommittal answer possible, try to shut and drive. Well, this argument is getting more and more heated, until finally, at a stoplight, the guy shouts: "Fine, bitch, I was just seeing you off, I'm glad you going!" Then he tosses me a twenty and gets out of the cab, while she screams "motherfucker" at his back out of the window. The light turns green, and I'm not quite sure what to do.

"Well, fucking drive," she says to the back of my head. Nice. I think the guy had the right idea. I drop her off, help her with the bags. She asks for the change from the twenty the guy threw me, then tips me 45 cents. The guy definitely had the right idea. I get back in the cab, restraining myself from giving her the finger, then head back up 17th to Cap Hill. I'm seventh in line, which means a good solid half an hour until my next fare, I've got a whopping twenty-three bucks, and the distinct urge to strangle the living shit our of someone which usually comes with day twelve in the cab. I find myself yelling "cut me off? I'll stab you in the fucking throat" at other cars and acting pretty much like the cliché cab driver. I need a break before I run my cab into a crowd of pedestrians. I head home and pull into a no parking zone near my house, turn on my hazards, and walk inside. I fill up my water bottle, take a piss, look out the window to make sure there's no parking cop sneaking up on my illegally parked cab, then collapse on the couch. Fuck. I'm stuck between pure rage at my job, a kind of pathological hatred and fear of my cab, and the need to pay off bills. I figure maybe I can take next Sunday off which would be seventeen days in a row. I sit there for a few minutes, feeling the fares tick away, know I might have already missed a call, maybe an airport run, maybe a car full of strippers looking for a good time, maybe more midgets, who knows. I can't sit there, I have to at least make my lease payment. Groaning, I try to psych myself up, get up and head out, the sun is beginning to set, so things might get better, but you never know. I get back in my cab, sit for a moment tapping the steering wheel and then realize I'm too amped up to wait for a fare. I need to drive. I kill the hazards, turn the key, and head out. I drive in a circle down Colfax to Pearl, turn right over to 17th, up 17th pass yuppie restaurants and gay bars up to Ogden, past the theaters, down Colfax past the hippie bars, and so on. I'm in front of some yuppie restaurant and get flagged down by a couple. They're heading to Wash Park, a good fare. The radio is playing some decent fast paced music, I have a long fare to a good zone, and a nice yuppie couple that'll probably tip decently. Smiling I head up 17th towards Park Ave, the night might work out after all. I'm turning onto Park Ave when it starts going bad.

"Well, that was fun," he says, not exactly sarcastically, more like he wishes, wants, and needs the night to have been fun. She shrugs noncommittally. "Didn't you have fun?" he asks, almost desperately.

"Not really," she replies petulantly, "Your friends don't really like me."

"Of course they do." I catch a note of desperation in his voice.

"No they don't. and my friends don't really like you." I hear her turn in her seat. "John, I just think we're too different." I almost snort out loud at this. They're about as different as two cloned mannequins from a Lands End catalogue. "I think we should just end this."

You have got to be fucking kidding me, I think, two goddamn breakups in my cab in one fucking night? I think of calling my cab "the breakup cab" or something.

"But…but I thought things were going well," he says in a kind of wimpy whine. I guess you were wrong, the voice in my head says.

"Well, they haven't been, I'm sorry, this just won't work out." Damn, shot down in flames, my little voice goes on. There is an uncomfortable silence as I turn onto 14th. I reach over surreptitiously to turn the radio up. Small increments, that's the key, be subtle, so they don't notice that you're trying to cover up the awkwardness.

"Are you sure?" he asks quietly. Great, just fucking great, only 27 more blocks to go.

"Yes." I can't see her, but I can tell by the tone of her voice that she has her arms crossed and is looking out the window and away from him. I hear a sniffle. God, the guy is crying, actually fucking crying, and I'm praying for green lights on University. Maybe I could call my cab "the crying cab". The last fifteen blocks is an uncomfortable montage of her sighing deeply, him sniffling, me slowly turning up the radio, and me doing my best not to yell at the guy to fucking man up.

I turn onto Mississippi and drop them in front of a nice house. He pays me, not meeting my eye, tips me well, and they walk off with him still trying to convince her to stay with him. The night has just begun, and my fares have left me feeling drained and depressed. I check the board and see that there's way too many cabs in the zone I'm in, and head back to Cap Hill. Sometimes nights just suck so much that you don't want to try anything outside of your usual routine. My golden spot is Cap Hill, even if some nights it just isn't working.

I actually get a fare quickly. I pull up in front of this building on 12th and Vine, no one is outside, so I call the number on my cell. I guy answers quietly, sounding down. Great, hope he's not on his way to break up with his girlfriend or something. I put the car in park, pop on the dome light, and start to read. He comes out a couple of minutes later. He's wearing a suit jacket, no tie, his hair a bit disheveled. He gets in the back, a little loosely. I put him about five or six cocktails into the evening, maybe a little more.

"Can we just drive?" He asks, kind of weakly, "just, you know, drive?" He holds up a credit card. "I got a credit card, go ahead and run it for whatever." I look at him over my shoulder, he seems straight up.

"Don't worry about it, we'll settle up when we're finished. Where you want to go?"

He leans back and sighs. "You know that liquor store on Colfax and Vine?'

"Sure."

I make a U-turn and head over towards Colfax. We pull up and he gets out.

"Don't leave me, OK?" He says as he opens the door.

"No problem, man, I'll be here." I put it into drive and watch the guy make his fairly steady way into the liquor store, wondering what I've gotten myself into. Might be a hell of a fare, might be a big pain in the ass, who knows? He comes back out with a pint bottle in a paper bag and gets in.

"Can I drink this in here?" Well, at least he's polite.

"As long as the cops don't see it," I reply, " and, if they do, I didn't know about it." I like to think that I'm a full service cab, I really don't care what you do back there , as long as it doesn't make a mess, mess with me, or get me in trouble.

"Fair enough." I hear the plastic on the cap crack, and him take a long drink.

"Where we going, man?"

"Hell, I don't know. Just turn on Colfax here, make it a right." I shrug and head east on Colfax.

"Can I smoke?" I nod and roll down his window. "Thanks, man," he says, sounding a little less sad, "you're all right." I see the reflection of his lighter igniting, and smell a hint of cigarette smoke. We drive a moment in silence.

"You know," he says pensively, "I've never been that far up East Colfax, don't even think I've been that far past Monaco."

"Want me to just head up there until you've seen enough? You know it's the longest street in the country, right?"

"Yeah," he says, laughing a bit. He taps me on the shoulder and holds up the bottle. "You want a hit of this?"

"No, that's cool, gotta drive, you know?" Actually some whiskey would be pure ambrosia, but that's a quick way to lose a driving job. Not that cops pull over cabbies, almost never happens unless you run a speed trap or drive over a sidewalk and a family of four.

"Yeah, wish I had that kind of will power." He sighs and leans back. "Going to jail tomorrow… fourth DUI." He leans forward, suddenly animated. "You see, I like driving drunk, just kind of driving around like what we're doing, helps me think. I guess I'm a dumb ass, huh?"

"Well," I consider my words for a moment, no need to piss this guy off. "You ain't driving now, right?"

"Yeah," he leans back again, "just wish I would have done this before. And most cabbies aren't as cool as you."

"Thanks."

"Sure," he takes another pull on the bottle. "Hey, can you turn the radio up?"

I turn it up and drive. I drive past Monaco, a random tour guide. Past strip malls and Mexican joints, past titty bars and highways, out to where the roads stop being alphabetized as much, then turn around and drive back. We stop at another liquor store on the way back, and as I pull in front of his apartment building, I realize he's asleep. I wake him with a gentle shake. He thanks me and has me put $95 on his card. I watch him stumble and weave up to his apartment lobby, then decide to call it a night for the crying cab and head home. As I'm getting out of the cab, I see that he left a full pint bottle in the back seat. Not one to look a gift bottle in the mouth, I grab it, open it on the way to my door, and take a long pull. As I thought, pure ambrosia.

I finish the pint bottle in short order, pouring it over ice into a large glass, swilling it down in the late night heat. I gulp it down on the front porch, sitting in my favorite chair, watching the beads of moisture roll down the glass reflected by the porch light. I top it off a few times until the bottle is empty, then toss the bottle in the general direction of the trashcan.

The whiskey burns at first, then goes down smooth as the ice melts. It's gone in what seems like moments, and I feel a fire, a burn beyond the whiskey. I need more, like it's water, like it's life itself. I check my cell, and see that I have three hours until last call.

Getting up, I feel the first pull of demon whiskey on my body, slightly unsteady, but full of joy. Fuck the crying cab. Fuck the sad people. Fuck the fuck ups, the assholes, the no tippers, the hot young things, they can all go to hell, I'm going to the bar. I feel like a gas fueled funny car ready for a tear, the night is young enough and I own it. Whiskey, my sweet god, I need more of you, until I fall of my barstool, until I howl at the moon and crap my pants. I want to write an ode to whiskey, a book, a fucking epic. I stumble off my porch and to the bar.

When I walk in, the wind is almost knocked out of my sails. Almost. There are three people at the bar, slumped down, doing the hunker, and my girl Josephine isn't bartending. Some newbie I don't recognize sits behind the bar looking surly. The dead sad pathetic energy of the place almost stops me in my tracks. Almost. I'm on a fucking mission, after all. I'm going to drink all of the fucking whiskey in town, if the whiskey here isn't good enough, sweet enough, or if, god forbid, they run out, I'll leave. There's a town full of whiskey out there, bar after bar of it, just begging to be drank. Bottles casting their coy eyes at me, shaking their sweet curves at me, full of amber goodness.

It's about time, I think as I sit at the bar. Why not? Maybe I'll be the sad sack in the back of some other poor fuck's cab. Huddled and weeping in the back seat, puking down the front of my shirt, laughing and slurring, speaking in tongues.

I down my first whiskey in one deep gulp feeling it burn my throat, lighting my soul like a flamethrower. I grin and motion the bartender over for another one. He eyes me fearfully. I think there's sweat standing out on my forehead, and my grin maybe more of a rictus, a stroke victim's grin. He pours me another, takes my money, and retreats to the other end of the bar, to lean against the bar and gossip with one of the barflies and occasionally glance in my direction.

Fine, I'm not wanted, there's a billion bars on Colfax and Thirteenth, and all of them have whiskey.

I have the feeling that somewhere in this great night is something big and amazing, looming over the horizon, just waiting at the next bar. What it is, I don't know. Could be true love, could be a night full of adventure, could be a suitcase full of money. I could end up in Las Vegas or under a bridge, on a park bench drinking mad dog with a pimp, or at the governor's mansion drinking fine fine cognac.

The point isn't what it could be. If I knew, that would ruin it. It's the mystery of the night, the magic of the unknown. All I know is that it isn't waiting at my usual bar, suddenly a stranger, boring and brimming with suspicion. I finish my drink, leave a good tip, and nod to the bartender. Out into the night, off for the great adventure, I cast my boat onto the mysterious whiskey river and set sail for new lands.

First thing needed when sailing to new lands on grand adventures is provisions. I stop at a corner liquor store and buy a pint bottle to attack on my way to fair land and new prospects. Sipping discretely as I wander down 13th I plan my route out. Down 13th to a few bars, then over to Colfax, and back up again. Hitting as many bars as needed until I can feel my hand on the throat of the night.

I ditch the half full pint behind a bush for quick and easy retrieval, and wander into a Goth bar on the corner of Penn and Thirteenth. My reserve falters at the door, one foot in, too late to back out. The bar's mostly empty. A chubby girl with dyed black hair, black lace clothes, and too much pancake makeup sits at the end of the bar. The bored kind-of-cute bartender talking to her, purple streaked hair glistening under the lights. A guy in rubber pants and a trench coat plays pool by himself — thrillsville.

It is too late to back out now, all eyes are upon me. So, with the slightest hesitation, I steady myself and make the long swim to the bar. I order a beer, and hunker down. There is no adventure here, just the faded Goth dream of vampires and tight fitting latex undergarments. I won't find what I'm looking for in this dim parody of a Lon Chaney movie. I finish the beer quickly, leave, and fetch my half empty pint bottle from the bushes, leaning over a slight bit too far and scraping my arm up on the branches.

I head, a bit less steady, a bit less careful with my swigs from the pint bottle, to the next bar, a music venue. The bottle is mostly empty, and I up end it in the alley behind the bar, swaying, only slightly, streetlights glinting off the bottle, a dim distorted vision of stars shining through the glass, then chuck it at a dumpster with a satisfying crash. On to the next bar! On to Glory!

I take a deep breath before I walk in, rallying the troops, steadying my gait. No need to reel in from the night, smelling of sweat and cab and whiskey. No need to run full on into the bar, no, no, need a good steady, adult demeanor.

Through the door I find myself in a dimly lit hell of acoustic guitars and self-congratulatory auditory masturbation- the open mic night. I pray that there's a good player as I walk up to the bar, pull up a seat and look around.

There's some aging hippie abusing a Bob Dylan tune on stage, and about five guys all with guitars, and a hangdog looking host. Is there no adventure in this town on a Tuesday night? I order a beer and a shot from a disgusted looking guy with a pompadour, and hope the next guy is better. He isn't.

While Robert Johnson is being flogged with an out of tune sixty-dollar guitar, I slam my drinks and make a hasty exit. I'm noticing that walking isn't as easy as it should be, and I still haven't found the promised land. Cursing Denver, and Tuesday, and June, I stagger north towards Colfax, and the land of fog and roses.

✿ ◉ ☉ ◎ ✿

I wake up full clothed, lying face down on my bed, not sure how the hell I got home. Whiskey hung-over and feeling like hell, I'm slightly drunk and tired like I didn't sleep at all. I'm sore, like I ran a marathon then got in a fight with a sumo wrestler, and I think I can drink about five gallons of water. The euphoria from the night before is gone with the whiskey, and I miss it. I remember vague images of several bars, maybe an argument. I have a general feeling of malaise and guilt. Just what the fuck happened after bar three I have no real clue.

All I know is that I didn't find that mystical El Dorado of drunken happenstance. Instead I wandered bar to bar, always with that feeling that something better lay over the next hill. Through the doors of the next dive bar or saloon, I went on a search for that elusive something, and, as usual, found nothing.

I stumble into the bathroom, rubbing my face and scratching different body parts. I lean over the sink and start running the cold water. I splash some on my face and then start gulping water from my cupped hands, over and over, until I feel like I'm swimming. I make a face and squeeze some toothpaste on my toothbrush. There's moss growing on my teeth and I think a sand blaster couldn't take it off, much less some plastic bristles.

I brush my teeth and gag on the minty taste. You know it's bad when brushing your teeth makes you want to puke. I quickly rinse my mouth out, cough, then swallow some more water and lean over the sink, swaying.

The taste won't go away, I realize. I understand that no matter how often I brush my teeth, my breath will still smell like I've been chewing on wino turds. I swallow a few more times, biting back the nausea. When I'm sure I'm not going to hurl, I walk downstairs and make some coffee.

Coffee- the life giver, the black liquid savior. I can feel it working its magic as I sit, eyes closed, and try to ignore the freight train slamming between my temples. The headache recedes a bit as the coffee goes down, my stomach decides that all it really needed was some water, and coffee isn't the enemy, thank god. Sometimes it's just the shock of waking up that's the worst. Your body reminding you that maybe another hour would be best and that you're an incredible dumb ass for putting that much booze through your system. But then you're up and about, a little more hydrated, a lot more caffeinated, and the hangover slinks away to hide under the blanket and glare at you, just out of sight.

I force myself to get motivated, I feel bad for putting off fixing Jody's bike, and, I have to admit to myself, I want to see her again. I get on the computer and look up a bike repair shop that's nearby, brush my teeth again, change my clothes, grab her bike, and I'm out the door, hangover and all.

I put her bike in the trunk, grab some string and tie it down so it doesn't bounce around too much, and head downtown. The toothpaste has already worn off and I'm pretty sure ,surrounding me like a cloud, is a heady mixture of vaporized whiskey and sour body odor. I roll down the windows. At this point I really don't care.

I drop the bike off at the shop, with a painful estimate on the price to fix it, book in, and park. My escapades from the night before have destroyed my windfall from the drunk driver, and I'm short on my lease for the day. I pull my hat down over my face, and lean back in the heat, feeling the booze leach out through my pores.

I'm fourth in line at two o'clock on a Wednesday afternoon, and nothing is moving. Fuck it, I think, fuck the bills, fuck my mortgage and my ex-wife, fuck my lease, fuck this cab. I think, for the thousandth time, of taking all of my money from the weekend, going to the bus station and taking the next bus out of town. Leaving the house, the job, everything behind, just starting over in a transient hotel in some far away city. But you can't do that anymore, the realistic part of my brain reminds me. They'll find you, track you through your social security number, your name, there is no more anonymity, no more freedom. The computer age is a chain around the ankle of escape. Run away, hop bail, they'll find you, somehow, they'll find you. So, it's just work, spend, get a credit card to cover the spending, work more to cover the credit card, build up credit, buy a house, go to college, spiral up that debt and put your nose to the grind stone. Forget hopes, forget dreams, just look to the next paycheck to pay the next bill and then work for the next paycheck.

Too hopped up on coffee, swimming in my own booze soaked

sweat, I can't sleep, so I start it up and drive towards downtown, hoping for a flag, maybe an empty taxi stand in front of a hotel. I turn down Eighteenth, then on to California, and am amazed at my luck. I see a bellhop waiving me down. I pull into the hotel's roundabout and see two stunning women, tall and slinky, and a short grizzled man come out of the hotel. They climb in all ass and legs, and give me stunning smiles. The man hops in the front.

"How much to go here?" He has an accent, maybe Eastern European. He is pointing at a lake on a hotel tourist map. Someplace I've never been, out past Englewood, south, near the mountains, west.

"Not sure, " I reply, "it's quite a ways."

"I give you a hundred to drive there, wait while we hike, then drive back."

I think about it, it'd probably be more than that to drive out and back with a tip, not to mention the wait. But there's no way I'd make that kind of cash on a Wednesday afternoon. I agree. After the drunk driver the night before and these European super models, I'm beginning to think I'm going to have one of those weeks where I could be sleeping in my cab and have a guy walk up and ask me if I could drive him to Aspen.

Some weeks are like that. It's like the streets are paved with dollar bills, and fares flagging you down everywhere you go, and other weeks all you get are hour waits, little old ladies at the grocery store, and no tipping bitchy welfare moms. I head out to this lake. I'm not quite sure of my route but know that they won't know or care. About twenty minutes later, I pull into the park, have the man pay the park ranger, and pull into the parking lot. They say they'll be back in about a half an hour and walk off. I take a deep breath of vanilla pine scented air, and feel nostalgic for boyhood camping trips. Although this manicured lake and park with paved hiking trails is a far cry from back country backpacking and cooking meals on an open fire. Back before everyone discovered Colorado, before fire bans and camping permits.

I sit at a picnic table for a bit, just enjoying the peace of the day. I know that there is a highway only half a mile away, but the sun is cooler than in the city, and there are birds other than pigeons singing in the trees. I get up and hike through the forest along a stream and feel at peace, the troubles of the day behind me for now. I walk for a while, head back to the cab and read until they come back, then drive into the city back to the hustle and bustle and hate. I drop them off at the hotel, take one last longing look at legs and ass, and head out to the motor to pay.

❀ ◉ ◎ ❀

I decided pretty early on not to care about why you're taking my cab. I just don't really care as long as you behave, pay, and tip. So there's no need to tell me "I'm paying my rent" or "just gotta meet this guy, he owes me money". I don't care. Really. Even if your rent involves me sitting outside of some sketchy row house while you score some crack. Or "paying your alimony" happens to be code for me sitting on a street corner while another car drives up and you hand some dude some cash and he palms you some mysterious package. Just don't get me involved, don't get me shot, and don't get me arrested. Plausible deniability, man. I try not to even look, except the occasional glance to make sure that you're still there. If the cops ask me, I just shrug- "He asked me to drive him here and wait." If I stopped and kicked out everyone doing something immoral or illegal I wouldn't make any fucking money at all, and that's the bottom line driving a cab- filthy filthy money. I am the underground ferry to the badlands, your glowing demon cab to Hell and addiction, a sweat-stained Charon on this asphalt river Styx. Whatever you need, wherever you're going, I'll get you there, just fucking pay me.

❀ ◉ ◎ ❀

Six hours later that moment in the park seems like a dream. I've spent most of the night either sitting on my ass or driving frantically to the next call. It's slow enough that I'm taking calls in Five Points even though I know most of them will be total bust no tippers. I'm driving up Downing after dropping off my latest fare of welfare mom and screaming kids, trying to get the hell out of Five Points and back on Capitol Hill where the pickings are slim, but at least polite and affluent.

The damn computer starts beeping, I hit confirm, and make a quick left, jog up 26th, and make a right on Williams. This is the border lands. I could get a good fare, some soon to be Yuppie gentrifyers, or I could get some sketchy crack run to the projects. I make the call and a scruffy unshaven guy in sweat pants gets out. A little from column A- a little from column B. He gets in the back, and I get a wave of a manic energy from him as he tells me to drive him to a rundown bar on Colfax near Colorado. Leaning towards column B now.

"Gotta grab me a hooker man." Farther over on column B. "Yeah, she's a great lay. It's my fortieth birthday. Gotta have it, man." The words flow out of him like some vicious verbal diarrhea. "She's a trip man, she's a trip. Gotta stop by her mom's house, get some drugs, man." Damn it, don't tell me. "She's a trip, but her mom." He finally pauses, takes a breath, for effect. "Her mom, man, now she's really a trip. Hooks out her daughter and sells coke to pay for her plastic surgery addiction."

OK, this guy has gone so far over to column B that I think he's into column C: crazy motherfucker that will leave me with a great story to tell the bartender. He just keeps babbling on and on, and I'm taking mental notes so I have a good story to tell Josephine next time I drink at her bar.

"Yeah," he rants leaning over the seat, stale coke breath blasting into my face, "she just sits up there in her apartment all wrapped up in bandages like the fucking Crypt Keeper. Skin all tight like some fucking alien, man." He doesn't need a response, he's in full on soliloquy mode. I just nod, grin, and drive. We pull up in front of the bar, and he hops out. "Be right back, man, wait to you see this girl, hot, man, hot, and man does she fuck, man does she fuck!" He runs into the bar, and I put it in park, shaking my head a bit.

He comes out a few minutes later with a rail thin girl in sweat pants with messed up hair, bad skin, and bad teeth. I suddenly feel sorry for this guy. This is his birthday dream date for the big four-oh, makes me feel sad for the whole fucking human race.

They get in. He gives me the next address, and he starts his run on sentence again. "Hey, man, you're mom's got it, right, I need at least forty. Ha forty for forty!" She tries to shush him. "No, no, don't worry about it, babe, me and him we're fucking tight. Used to work together." He gives me a conspiratorial wink in the mirror. "Oh, me and him go way back, way fucking back." It's only a few blocks to the apartment building. I pull in and park. He tosses me a twenty. "Don't worry my man, we'll be right back. That's for you right now, keep the meter running, man." She starts to walk off, and he leans back in, I get another wash of coke breath, like rotting snot and vomit. "Freak show man, time for the freeeeeeak show." He pulls his cheeks back and makes a face. "Fucking Crypt Keeper man." He does a quick calculating pause. "You wanna come up, check it out?" I find myself tempted by the offer. He sees me think about it, and leans further in. "You gotta see it, you'll kick yourself if you miss out on something this strange." Against my better judgment, I get out of the car.

"That's the spirit, my man!" He chuckles and I follow him and the girl into the high rise lobby. We stand a moment in awkward silence waiting for the elevator; I feel a sense of anticipation, like waiting to have the curtain pulled back at an old fashioned freak show.

The elevator door opens slowly, and we get in. The elevator is tight and hot, and I can smell an acrid tang of liquor, cigarettes and stale sweat from my two companions. The guy hums nervously under his breath, while the girl fidgets adjusting her overlarge t-shirt and brushes the hair that has escaped from her shabby pony tail out of her face. The tension seems to build as the elevator rises slowly, and I feel sweat break out in my armpits and across the brim of my hat. I want to take my hat off and wipe my forehead with my arm, but I resist the temptation. It's like we're on our way to meet some Byzantine despot or maybe the devil himself. As the ancient elevator creaks inexorably upwards, lights flickering, I begin to second guess my choice to come up.

Separate, I think, separate. I have to keep distance from my customers or fall into their madness. I was failing with that with Carrie, and here I was. I'm feeling control slowly crumble away and can see a future where I'm driving around screaming like a madman, taking hits off the pint in my pocket and doing lines off of the dashboard of my trusty police interceptor until I spin, inevitably, out of control in a fiery crash. I'm drenched in sweat and I can see my male companion, I never did get a name, trembling visibly, whether in ecstatic anticipation or terror, I can't tell. The door finally pings and slides jerkily open. The hallway seems over lit and ornate after the dim dingy elevator. The mad pattern of the carpet strikes my eyes as we exit the elevator, the girl first, then him, then me, hesitant. We walk to door 614 and the girl knocks twice quickly, I hear a croaking voice from within and she opens the door.

The small crowded apartment strikes me as something like a transvestite's dressing room before a drag show: Pink wall paper, ornate white dressing table with a lighted mirror, framed pictures of celebrities, and a large four poster bed framed with white and pink lacy gauze.

She lies on the bed, arms by her side, propped up in a Snow White kind of pose, dressed in a frilly pink nightgown. The skin on her face is pulled tight until her semi-focused eyes seem almost oriental against her powdered white skin. Her mouth is pulled back in a clown-lipped rictus, and her breasts jut up, impossibly perky and bullet like. The nightgown is cinched tight around a corset-thin waist and the air is heavy with cigarette smoke.

"Who the hell is that?" She asks in a voice like grinding gears, hand pointed imperiously at me.

"Oh, he's an old buddy of mine," my nameless friend responds, voice full of bravado. The room seems to close in on me and the smoke makes my throat itch. I regret coming up, I mean, what the fuck am I doing here?

"Well, I don't fucking know him," she grumbles and begins to cough a rasping phlegmy cough. I feel sweat begin to trickle down my spine and into my underwear.

"He's cool, he's cool."

"Hey," I say, feeling the need to be somewhere, anywhere, else.

"No problem, I'll just wait in the cab."

"Come on," he says, elbowing me lightly in the ribs, "it's no problem." He lowers his voice. "I was going to get you a bump, man."

"No," I shake my head, "I'm good." I turn and open the door. "I'll be downstairs."

I make a hasty exit and half stumble down the hall. The air in the elevator seems light and breezy compared to the stinking bizarre miasma of the woman's apartment. The elevator stops in the lobby and I almost run to the cab. What the fuck was I thinking? Stay separate, don't let their insanity carry you along, don't join the madness. I'm just here to ferry them from one fucked up bit of their life to the other fucked up bit. No need to get involved.

I open the cab door and sit with a sigh, feet outside the cab. I take my hat off and wipe my head, then put my face in my hands, rubbing my eyes. I shake my head, pull my legs into the cab and shut the door. That was seriously fucked up. I consider leaving them there, but decide I can deal with them a little while longer, as long as the clownish Barbie doll mummy doesn't come along. Besides, as always, I need the money.

A few minutes later my phone rings. I curse silently to myself as I reach for it. Never fails, a dead fucking night and the minute you get a long fare, a regular calls you. I look at the caller ID and it's Carrie. I feel a quick start of lust as I answer. Aw, hell, maybe I will leave them here.

"Hey, Carrie, what's up?"

"Whatcha doing?" She sounds upbeat again, I feel a bit of my pulse in my throat, flashing back to pink fishnets and a tattooed neck.

"Waiting for a crack head and his hooker to pick drugs up from a woman who is addicted to plastic surgery, and you?"

"Really?" She giggles.

"I shit you not, never a fucking dull minute around here."

"Oh, um, can you grab me and take me to work?"

"I'd love to," really love to says my crotch, "it's going to take me about forty depending Sir Cracksalot here."

"That's fine, I'm at the place on Marion."

"OK, be there as soon as I can."

"Thanks. Bye." There's a bit of chirp in the "bye" and I'm sure she's working me, but I just can't help myself.

I hang up, and lean back and my seat, absentmindedly rubbing my half-chub and check the time and meter. They've got ten minutes. Then I leave and pick up my pink haired waif.

They make my deadline by two minutes, staggering back to the car arm and arm.

"Back to your place?" I ask as they settle in. He frowns. All manic energy seems to be driven out of him. Like he had a sudden realization of where he was.

"No," he sighs, "no, take her back to the bar."

"What the hell?" she argues in a shrill voice, "I thought we were going to have a good time?"

"What do you care?" Sullenly, "You got your cut."

The drive back to the bar is silent. I pull in front of the bar and she gets out slams the door and gives him the finger. He has me take him back to his place. He is silent. I guess the drugs have worn off or turned on him. I expect he'll spend an introspective night at home smoking coke and wondering what the hell happened to his life. Or, more likely, he'll get high and manic again, call another cab, and do the same again. Rinse, Lather, Repeat. I drop him off, he tips well, I thank him, and he waves me off with a half-hearted gesture. I gun it down Downing towards Carrie's house. As I drive I try to figure out how I should act: eager, smooth, comfortable? I am at a loss, it could be awkward, could be fine, I mean she called me. I've been out of the dating scene for so long I don't know how to act and react. Not like that getting a BJ in my cab for ten bucks counts as dating. I realize I'm being neurotic, and to just act like nothing happened.

I give her a heads up and she's waiting for me in the alley when I pull up. She's dressed sedately, for her: torn jeans, studded belt, combat boots and a too large for her black Ramones t-shirt. I guess when you spend most of work naked it doesn't matter much what you wear. She gets in back, my first let down, tossing her bag first.

"Howdy, cowboy!" The cab fills with jungle flower smell, a great respite from the last fare of bad breath, B.O. and desperation.

"How ya doin' sugar?' I drawl. She smiles, and I put it in drive. She's silent for the trip, I glance into the mirror, and see she's putting on make-up, a little too much, a little too bold. She looks painfully young at that point, and I am almost ashamed of my lust. Almost, but not quite. She catches me looking at one point, and blows me an overdramatic kiss. I turn the radio up, and cruise down Park Avenue, sedate but disappointed that nothing will happen tonight. I pull in front of the strange Victorian porn shop and put it into park. She hustles out, then leans in the window.

"How much?" she asks, all lipstick and eyelashes.

"Whatever." I say. I'd kept the meter open, so I could catch another fare, I do that on slow nights with my regulars. Really. She raises her eyebrows suggestively. I almost feel myself blush. "Make it ten." She smiles, hands me 15 and kisses me on the cheek, leaving a red smear that I won't find out about for hours.

"I get off at five, you still going to be driving?" I think about it, but know way better, that'd put me at fifteen hours, I wouldn't even be up for a blowjob much less driving around at that point.

"No, I might call it early tonight, kind of slow." She looks disappointed, but shrugs.

"Well, I'll just have to call some other cabbie." She winks at me and sashays into the porn store. I feel kind of like a moron for the stab of jealousy I had at that statement. I try to shrug it off and head down to LoDo to see if there are any early weekday drunks ready to head home early.

I call it a night around two, giving up on the last of a nonexistent bar rush, park about four blocks from my house and walk home, enjoying the light breeze after the stifling heat radiating off of the cab's engine. It's quiet, the trees silhouetted against the streetlights, no traffic, no lights on in the houses. I feel like the only person alive on the planet, as I walk up the stairs to my porch. I sit on the steps for a moment before I go in, stretching my legs, twisting my neck trying to get the kinks out.

I am overwhelmed by the desire for the plain creature comfort of another human being just wanting me. Lying in a bed with a woman, just touching, soft hands kneading the kinks out of my muscles, resting my head on a firm thigh as fingers run through my hair, just being naked for the hell of it. I feel a great pain well up out of my gut and I feel like throwing myself into the street.

I get back up and walk back to my cab, just wanting to drive, meter off. As I drive around on the dead streets aimlessly, I suddenly feel kin with my "drunk driver" passenger of a few days ago. I know what he was after, what he was feeling. Too often I drive like a hunter after prey. I forgot the enjoyment that comes from just feeling the road under my wheels, the steering wheel in my hand, the empty city. I drive, not waiting for lights to turn, just making right turns, or left when I feel like it. I feel a bit of the stress from life leaving me, as I ease the seat back a bit.

After a half an hour or so I find myself parked in front of the Victorian porn store. It almost seems like a dream as I get out and walk in, buy some tokens and go into the booth. It is hot and cramped and smells like spunk and beer. Hands shaking, I put in a token and the panel slides back, and there she is, like a porn store Aphrodite rising from the waves. She's naked, another tattoo, this of a tiger, on her hip. I see that her nipples are pierced, and that she's shaved. The room seems overwhelmingly hot, the walls too close, claustrophobic. She dances slowly to some unheard music, and I feel dizzy. She looks at the glass, and even though I know she can't see me, I feel like she looking through me, into my rotted soul. Panicking, I get up and race out of the store, earning an odd look from the tired looking clerk. I lean against my cab, feeling like I'm going to vomit, take a few deep breaths, get in my cab and drive home.

❀ ◉ ◉ ◉ ❀

I'm woken up by my phone ringing around nine in the morning. Cursing, I roll over and thrash around at my nightstand, knocking over empty beer cans, tossing my alarm clock onto the floor, all in a futile attempt to find my cell phone. By the second ring I realize that it's in my pants. Staggering, I get up, dig through piles, trying to find my jeans. Triumphantly holding them up, I dig the phone out of the pocket just as it stops ringing. I look cross-eyed at the missed calls, and don't recognize the number. I stumble over to my bed and lie down. Just as I start to drift off, the message alarm goes off. Grunting, I roll over and dial my voice messages. It's the bike shop, the bike's ready. Great, couldn't they have waited until two to tell me that? Stuffing the phone under my pillow. I roll back over and go to sleep.

The rest of the day's sleep is stop start stop start, like rush hour traffic. I just get to sleep as the neighbor decides it's time to work on his lawn. The starting lawnmower jolts me out of sleep, then the constant hum lulls me back. A while later a loud Harley wakes me up again, and I lie there deciding whether or not it is worth it to try to get more sleep; to lie there until I get back to sleep, probably only to wake up again. The loud echoing crash of freight trains banging together, being carried across miles of cityscape by summer acoustics, decides it for me. No more sleep today, it's ten o'clock and I got to bed a little after four, so be it. I get up, make coffee, and call Jody. She says she'll meet me at her apartment around noon. I putz around the house for a bit, half-heartedly cleaning up, then drive down to the bike shop, pick up her bike, and drive out to the DU area.

She answers the door in tan shorts and a halter top, her straw colored hair done up in a ponytail, the all American girl look. I hand her the bike, trying not to look down at her tanned legs, and the bit of downy blonde hair down on her thighs.

"Good as new", I say. She holds the bike, smiling, for a moment as I think of something to say. "How's the knee?'

"Healing good, doc," she replies, and holds her knee up for me to look at. I get a good look at her slightly scabbed knee and golden thigh. Ah, jeeze, try not to look and... "I've had much worse, when I used to rock climb..." She stops and I wonder if our entire time together is going to be uncomfortable moments and things we don't want to talk about.

"Um," I clear my throat, "yeah. Well, it was great seeing you, hope I run into you again, without, you know, running into you." She smiles slightly, lame joke. I start to walk away.

"Hey." I turn back.

"You want to get some coffee or something? You know catch up?" I find I'm smiling a big smile.

"That'd be nice. When's good for you?"

"How's tomorrow, I have it off, so whenever's good for you, I know you work nights-"

"How's one tomorrow afternoon?"

"Great." She smiles, hesitates, then waves and wheels the bike inside. I look back for a moment, then walk back to my cab, feeling a lift in my spirits. Kind of a date? Maybe a date? Do I want a date? I have no answers to the questions, but I know I feel happier than I've felt in a long time, so decide not to complicate things by asking stupid questions that I don't want the answer to.

✿ ◎ ◎ ✿

Sometimes it's like you're more bouncer than driver. People are drunk, and you have to talk them down, break up fights, and sometimes, you have to get physical and actually bounce someone out of your cab. Doesn't happen all that often, and I'm a fairly level headed guy, at least I'd like to think so. But, every so often, some asshole pushes my buttons, and that's it, they're off on the side of the road, no matter where the fuck I am. From comments that I've had from my customers, I do this a lot less than some of the other cab drivers. One of the more common comments is: "I don't know how you put up with this shit." Well, truth be told, quite often I don't. But, usually, no matter how big an asshole someone is being, I still want their damn cash. So I put up with as much as possible for that last dollar, and sometimes it actually works, and their friend or even the asshole, tips well, just for putting up with them. Sometimes.

Once, on a cold blizzardy night in February, I had a guy frantically flag me down on Seventeenth Street. I pulled over, trying not to slide, since the roads were pure hell. He ran and got in back, just as some crazed bum in a ratty coat tackled him yelling "where's my goddamn money". I looked in the mirror, to see if my fare was holding his own. He wasn't. He was lying on his back in my backseat, pushing his feet at the guy to keep him back, while the bum struggled and snapped at him like a rabid lemur. Sighing. I put the cab in park, got out, grabbed the bum by his coat and the belt of his pants and heaved him into Seventeenth, getting a good wif of what must have ode de urine and rubbing alcohol.

Luckily for him, traffic was minimal as he slid across two lanes on his ass, and then scrambled to get up. I calmly shut the door, got in front and drove away, as the guy righted himself in the backseat.

"Thanks man, I have no idea who that guy is, he just started following me and yelling about money."

I drove him home, a short fare, he tipped miserly. Rude, but what you gonna do?

❁ ◉ ◎ ❁

Thursday. Thursdays can be great nights, or can be slow as hell, mine is somewhere in between. I feel the six hours of sleep pretty strongly, and pull into a 7-11 for a pick me up. I gave up on midnight coffee a while ago, it just made me jittery and then I couldn't sleep at the end of the night even worse than normal.

I get out of the cab, stretching and twisting, hearing the vertebrae pop, and make my way on unsteady sea legs into the store. I grab a B vitamin loaded juice and some nuts and buy ten bucks worth of gas. As I put the gas in, I keep checking my computer to make sure no bells have come through, then climb back in and slug some of the juice. I find that B vitamins give me a decent pick me up, and at least make me feel a little more awake.

I pull away from the pumps and rub my eyes with the heel of my hand. They feel like heavy lead weights stuck in my head. Yawning, I turn up Colfax looking for bar fares. I go by the Squire, the Satire, and Lion's Lair, hoping that some of the clowns outside smoking are actually looking to flag down a cab. No luck, so I turn right on York, left on 14th, then left on Josephine, then another left on Colfax, keeping an eye out for people in front of the sports bar on the corner. Nada. I drive back down Colfax looking and looking for fares. Either no one is out or no one is ready to go home yet. I decide to park it and take a nap when I get a computer call.

I pick the fare up at a high-end restaurant on Seventeenth and take them to a nice house in Cherry Creek. I'm heading back towards Capitol Hill when I get a call from the next zone over, away from Capitol Hill, towards Wash Park. I take it, but curse under my breath, since it's kind of a bitch to do a U-turn on Josephine where it turns into University.

I go five blocks north, away from my fare until I can turn down a side street, then onto York, then south to where York and Josephine merge and become University. I try to gun it through lights, because this fare has all of the feeling of an old bell. For one thing it went to an adjoining zone, which means there were no available cabs in that zone, then I have to drive ten blocks out of my way, and it's about twenty blocks away. Half the time, you'll get there and they'll be tired of waiting and gotten a ride, called another company, or flagged down a cab. Still, it's not that busy, and I need the money, especially after paying for Jody's bike repair. Of course I'm stuck at the light at University and First, an interminably long light when you're rushing to get money.

The light finally changes, and I start lane jockeying to get around slow moving dipshits. I get a clear lane and hit about ten over the speed limit, which you can do on University because the lights are few and far between. I make the light on Alameda and cruise the next seventeen blocks to my fare, pulling up into a bus stop in front of a rundown bar I've never been to before. I call again, and the bartender yells over the noise saying the guy is on his way out. I put it in park, and lean back. I'm a little amped from the B vitamins and the pell-mell drive, so I find myself drumming my fingers on the steering wheel in time to the music on the radio.

After a few minutes the guy comes out. He's a fucking mess. He's stumbling a bit and trying to straighten his shirt out, but at least he's not pissed stained and covered in vomit. He comes up to the front door, and yanks it open, then looks startled, like he's surprised at his own strength. I quickly move all of my front seat crap out of the way and he piles in, grinning. I turn on the meter while he struggles with the seat belt, then watch him continue to miss. This happens more than you'd think. I sigh, then reach over and hook it up for him. He turns and looks at me with an idiot grin, eyes glazed and unfocused. I wait for him to tell me where we're going, he keeps staring at me with the idiot grin. Great.

"So, where we going?" He looks at me for a bit, then answers, like he's listening to an echo.

"Will's house." I wait… no more. Fucking great.

"Well. Where's Will's house at?" My voice is pitched like I'm talking to a four year old. Again the pause.

"You know, Will's house."

"No, I don't. I don't know Will."

"You don't know where Will's house is?" I'm tempted to boot him out right there, but hesitate.

"Just drive that way." He points down University and, for some reason, I put it in drive and go. After about ten blocks he starts tapping me on the shoulder.

"Here, here, here," he yells frantically. I turn quickly across traffic.

"Gotta give me warning man. Where next?"

"That way for a while." I drive for a bit, when I hear him snoring. I look over and he's asleep, head leaning back, a bit of drool running out of his mouth. Pissed, I make a sharp right cranking it hard. He slides over and bangs his head against the window, startling him awake.

"Where am I going?" I ask.

"Will's house!" I'm getting pretty sick of the "who's on first base" routine.

"Where the fuck is Will's house?"

"Turn left here." I turn then go a few blocks.

"Do I turn here?" I look over and he's asleep again, I swerve the cab and bang his head against the window again. He starts awake.

"Where the fuck am I taking you? Give me an address if you're going to pass out."

"We're going to Will's house. What are you fucking stupid?"

I've had enough and pull quickly over to the curb, get out, grab him by his booze soaked shirt and haul him out of the cab like a two hundred pound flounder.

"Give me five bucks," I growl into his face. He fishes out a fiver and hands it to me. I shut the passenger door and go back around to my side. I'm about to get in when he gives me a bewildered look.

"Where am I?" He looks around.

"You're at fucking Will's house." I get in and drive off, leaving him on a random street corner in a random neighborhood, and head back to Capitol Hill. Hell, he's most likely got a cell phone, either he'll find his way home or to the drunk tank. Not my problem. A man can only take so much.

❀ ◉ ◎ ◉ ❀

I'm thinking about calling it a day around midnight, exhausted and cranky, in no condition to deal with another drunk. I don't even feel like going to the bar for a drink. I'm heading back to my house vowing to stop working if I don't get a call before I get home. I'm about two blocks from my place when my cell phone rings. Great. I look quickly and see that it's Carrie. Well, it could be worse. I answer.

"Hey, it's Carrie."

"What's up?"

"I need a favor... I need to grab some stuff from a place I was crashing at, can you pick me up downtown?"

"Sure." She gives me a street corner outside of Lodo and I head downtown.

She's standing on the corner looking faded and small, drawn into herself. She wearily climbs in and gives me an address near Globeville, total sketch town. We take the drive in silence, her looking out the window and fidgeting, a slight twitch every now and then. I pull up in front of a boarded up storefront.

"This is it," she points out laconically, but doesn't get out. She turns to me, and I can see her eyes are nervous. There is a stretching pause.

"Can you come in with me? It's kind of sketchy, and it'd make me feel better."

I hesitate, then nod roll up the windows, and turn off the motor, pocketing the keys. We walk up to the door, and I can detect no lights, the door opens, unlocked, and we walk into a dark hallway with narrow stairs covered in dogshit brown dusty carpeting, worn through to the padding in spots, leading up.

The light is out in the hallway, the only light coming from dim streetlights outside, and a bare bulb dangling on the second floor hallway. The thought that Carrie has taken me here to rob me, set me up, crosses my mind like a spike of fear. I think about how much cash I have on me, a little over a hundred, and start to sweat.

She takes me by the hand and leads me up the stairs, and I feel like I'm lost in a helpless dream, floating, no control, preordained. The stairs squeak and give, the smell is of a boarding house gone to disuse, full of dust and cooking grease. My heart beats in my throat as we mount the top stair, and I look down another narrow hallway. It's lit by a bare dim 50 watt bulb, with the same dogshit carpet with yellow padding showing through.

We walk to a brown door, lock scratched, battered and broken, pale wood grain showing through a multitude of random cut lines in the dark brown veneer. She turns the glass doorknob and walks in, me trailing behind, alert, ready for the crushing blow in the back of my skull.

As we walk in, the smell of sewage, unwashed humanity, and vomit hit me like a wave. We walk into a long room lit by a single desk lamp, with people lying on piss stained mattresses and piles of blankets, seemingly scattered at random. There's maybe ten people lying in piles, nodding off leaning against the wall, some with feral glances in our direction, some completely unaware of us. A young white guy, rail thin and pale, with a stained yellow and green striped shirt, like some lost and fucked up Linus, nods at Carrie.

We tip-toe almost, stepping over used needles and empty beer cans, light bulbs with the filaments removed, sodden linens, and dirty clothes, to a corner by an open bathroom door showing a broken and puke stained toilette. I've never been to a place like this, and it's like staring into an open cesspool that leads all the way to hell.

Carrie reaches behind the door, and pulls out a thick photo album, letting out what seems to be a sigh of relief. We quickly make our way out of the room, and I'm tempted to back out as we reach the door. The stale air in the hallway is almost a relief after the miasma of the shooting gallery. Carrie quickly runs down the stairs and I follow her, not letting out my breath until we are back in the cab.

"What the fuck was that place?" I find myself asking, even though, deep at my core, I know.

"You don't want to know, cowboy, you don't want to know." She is clutching the photo album to her chest, and seems flushed and alive again. "Just drive back towards Capitol Hill, OK?"

I'm more than ready to agree, and roll down the windows, still feeling like there is some noxious odor clinging to me, to us.

We're cruising through the darker parts of Park Hill, when she tells me to pull over.

"Turn on the dome light." I do. "Want to see what it is?"

"Sure." She hands me the album and I opened it. I had assumed it was priceless family photos, but it's a hodgepodge of photos, no one person looking the same. As I flip through it, I see some photos that look like the came right out of a store bought picture frame. I'm beginning to become pissed off that we went through that madness to get this bizarre artifact.

"You see," she says breathlessly, "I don't have much of a family, I left young, and don't want anything to do with them, so I built this. I dumpster dive the pictures, find them whereever, and make up a past, a story for each one, they're my make believe family. Each one has a story. That's Uncle Mort," she points to a balding man in a photo from the Seventies, "he's a used car salesmen, with a secret cross dressing fetish."

She points to another, and comes up with another outlandish story for it. I look up at her, illuminated by the harsh light of the dome light, and she seems both younger and horribly older than I had first assumed. She stops, looks up and sees me watching her.

"You think I'm nuts." Which I kind of do, but in an almost touching kind of way.

"No, no, it's cool, kind of artistic." She cocks her head at me.

"Yeah?"

"Yeah." She pulls the album back and closes it, reaches up and turns off the dome light. She leans close, and there's that jasmine again.

"Wanna do it? Right here, right now, cowboy?" She whispers it closely, into my, ear, tickling, making the hairs on my neck stand up, a shiver run down my spine.

"Sure," I say, wanting to sound nonchalant, my throat suddenly dry, my pants tight. She giggles and reaches into her purse, pulling out a bright green condom. She reaches over, and yanks the buttons on my jeans open, pulling down on them, sudden, almost frantic. I look around at the quiet blank-windowed houses as I help her pull my jeans and underwear down to my knees, and wonder if they ever imagine that things like this go on in their nice neighborhood, just outside their safe and normal lives. She quickly pulls her panties down over her thigh-high stockings and sidles over to me as I lean the seat back. Her back to me, leaning over the steering wheel. She hikes up her skirt and slides onto me, me into her. I can feel the heat of her, almost in an abstract way, through the latex of the condom. She starts to bob up and down on me, gripping the steering wheel. Some cretin in the back of my head notes that it's good that the horn in my cab is broken. She grinds away and my legs start to tingle, and it feels good and awkward, embarrassing and odd all at the same time. I watch her trim ass slide up and down, my penis a clown-

like green. Her skirt tucked up, my legs going numb. Her holding
the steering wheel, and making little grunting noises, while at any
moment a cop could drive by or some citizen on a late night dog
walk might stroll by and see us boning away. I almost want to laugh
out loud at the madness and excitement. Instead, I grab her waist
forcing her up and down quicker and quicker and her grunts turn to
moans, then to squeaks, than to damn near shouts. As we increase
tempo, the car shakes and squeaks and I'm sure that the whole
neighborhood will come awake to see what all the ruckus is about,
and them I'm coming, earth shattering, and I just don't fucking care
anymore.

❁◉◉❁

I wake to the shrill beeping of my cell phone's alarm and roll
over, confused. I usually don't even bother with setting an alarm, just
get up and go whenever I wake up. I pick it up and look at the calen-
dar notice, suddenly remembering coffee with Jody. A nice normal
thing to do —coffee with an all American girl, no pink hair, heroin,
and fucking in my cab. As I shower and scrub myself clean, I'm
struck by the dichotomy between my day and my night life. Driving
my cab seems to be a downward spiral into the dark side of society, a
maelstrom of strangeness, booze fueled madness, and bizarre sexual
fetishes. While daytime is a nice coffee date, something normal
people with normal jobs do. People who mow their lawns and have
bar-b-ques on the weekend, not mad hermits who shun the light of
day.

I rest my head against the cold tile as the heat of the shower
hits me and wonder just what the fuck is going on. Where whatever is going on with Carrie is leading me to, where the odd flirty
awkwardness with Jody is going. Whether I can handle any more of
this insane life. I'm beginning to look at my cab with fear every time
I step off my front porch, will it lead me to money or to madness, or
both? I turn the shower off, dry myself and get dressed, putting on a
nice shirt for once, and do what I always do — let life take me by the
horns and do what it will, like a mind-numbed soldier marching off
to some lunatic Stalingrad.

✲⊙⊙⊚✲

I drive up to the coffee shop, and the sun is bright and soft filtering through the trees on Seventeenth. This just seems to make matters worse. I hate it when the weather doesn't agree with my moods, in fact has the gall to come across opposite. The weather should be dark and murky, not bright and beautiful. After hunting around for a parking space, I park and walk the two blocks to the coffee shop, birds whistling in bright pastels, mocking my mood. I feel like I should be in a fucking Disney movie with some bird landing on my shoulder and singing a song about what a beautiful day it is right before shitting on my shoulder and flying away.

She's already there sitting on the patio, sunglasses on, pastels and dirty blonde hair, soaking in the light, reading. As I walk up, I notice the book is "Abnormal Psychology" of all fucking things.

"Little light reading?" I ask, smiling, trying to shake the odd sense of doom that has been following me around like a cloud since I woke up. She looks up and gives me a radiant smile over the top of the book.

"Going back to school in the Fall, thought I'd bone up a bit."

"Ah. I'm going to grab a cup of coffee, be right back."

I walk into the coffee shop, look around at the art and order a cup of iced coffee from the bored looking college student behind the counter. Going back to school, decent job, a future, what the hell is she having coffee with me? Someone stuck in a dead end job, divorced, can't even pay his bills. Maybe I'll go back to school get a Masters… yeah, I can't even get motivated enough to mow my front lawn, much less fill out enrollment paperwork, apply for student loans, and take my GRE's. I get my cup of coffee and go back outside, sitting down opposite of her, back to the sun.

I lean back and sip the coffee, enjoying the bitterness of flavor combined with sensation of cool.

"So, how was work last night?" She asks, innocently enough.

The thought of answering truthfully crosses my mind. Something like: "Well, I went to some strange drug den to retrieve a album full of stranger's pictures, then screwed a teenage punk rock junkie in the front seat of my cab, and you?" I decide against that tactic.

"Oh, you know, same as usual," I mime driving with my hands, "driving a bunch of drunks around."

"Oh, come on, can't be all that boring, you have to have some interesting things happen in your cab." I run through some of the things that have happened, and decide they're all just a little too strange and depraved for bright sunny coffee conversation.

"Sometimes, sure, but most of the time it's just driving and dealing with really, really drunk people."

"Oh." She seems a bit disappointed, so I quickly tell her the about the guy who just wanted to drive, then about the overly clean woman I had in my cab right before I ran into her. Soon the stories are coming out. Not all of them, of course, but enough that I realize that I need to get them off my chest, put some sort of sense into them, have some sort of catharsis to clear my head. At some point in my story telling I realize that she'd make a great psychologist, and feel a little more than scared of her.

We end up chatting for about an hour when I get a call from a regular and have to go. Somehow, before I leave we agree to make another coffee date, and I don't know exactly how I feel about that.

❀ ⊙ ⊙ ❀

Ever had one of those days that seems like a déjà vu? Like you've gone through the all the same motions and actions over and over, nothing new, just slightly reminiscent of something that has happened before? That was what my day was like, that's what my life had turned into, except for the occasional bout of weirdness. Déjà vu with occasional weirdness, sounds like a Jonathan Lethem novel. I guess that's not exactly déjà vu; the feeling that you've done everything before, over and over again. The French probably have a term for it, déjà blah or something. Either way, turn left, turn right, laugh with customers, fight with customers, it was all the same. Dull. My cab felt like the enemy, even that fine glass of whiskey at the end of my shift seemed route and tired. I left it half-finished on my porch and went to bed.

✿◉◎✿

I dream that I'd captured a leprechaun, all green vest, hat, red beard, and stereotypical bad brogue. I demand to taken to his pot of gold, he does a jig, smiles and leads me onto a stage straight out of a The Price is Right. On each side of a massive cast iron cauldron stand Carrie and Jody, overly made up, coffered, wearing tight sequined game show hostess dresses. Bright vacant smiles pull at their lips, gleaming Vaseline teeth glitter and wink at me. They hold out their arms to present my great prize. I walk towards it, greed glistening in my heart, and peer over the edge. It is filled to the brim with greasy tartar sauce… now what the fuck does that mean?

✿◉◎✿

She waddles up to my, cab, holding her distended belly in one hand and an overnight bag in the other. I scurry out of the cab and hold the door for her as she hands me the bag. She eases in and holds out her hand for her bag.

"Take me, to the hospital, I'm having my baby," she says to me as I hand her the bag. I quickly shut the door, and scurry even faster to the drivers' door. Son of a bitch.

I head towards the hospital complex, then remember to ask which hospital. She tells me, and only then do I remember to turn on the meter. A baby, great. I'm hustling, but not blowing any stop signs or anything. It's something that happens to cab drivers in movies all the time, but not something I'd ever expected to happen. You'd think I'd be excited, bringing new life into the world, and all that crap. But I'm more focusing on whether or not her water has broken, and what a fucking mess it'll be if she hasn't. Or, even worse, if she does give birth in the back, having to hose all that shit and placenta off the seats. A definite day breaker for sure. I can see picking up that fucked up mental patient I had the week before. I'm imagining her saying: "What's that smell?" and me replying: "Oh, that? Just some afterbirth, blood, and feces, mind the umbilical cord, please." Shit, something like that'll just fuck your day right up, take hours to fix, or you might just have to call it a day until the cab has aired out. I turn onto Downing and hit the curves just right as she moans loudly.

"Almost there," I say helpfully.

"No, not the emergency room, maternity entrance, on 19th," she says, irritated.

"Sorry, sorry," I say and turn up 21st. Like I've ever had to deliver someone to the maternity entrance. I go up 3 blocks, past the hospitals, then over to 19th, and back down again. I hit a light and sit there, fingers tapping on the steering wheel, wondering if my whole back seat comes off, so I can hose underneath.

"There, there," she points as we speed down 19th. She hands me $15 as we pull into the entrance. "Keep it."

I put it in park, and race around, opening the door and helping her out, holding back a loud sigh of relief as I see the dry back seat. I help her and her bag to the door, hand her over to a nurse, and head back to the cab. That's the thing about this job, all the things that are a wonder in life are something to be feared or avoided, because either they're messy or they don't make you money. I book back in, and slowly pull out onto 19th.

❁ ◉ ◉ ❁

I'm driving through downtown, now empty and ghost-like, knowing I should call it a night. The wind is blowing warm and dry, as empty food wrappers and plastic cups roll through the streets like garbage tumble weeds across an empty prairie of asphalt. I turn up 22nd, and towards Park Avenue, where the nice part of downtown starts fading into rundown ramshackle buildings with Spanish signs advertisings food, day labor, and buses to Mexico and Guatemala. These buildings mix in with new Yuppie condominium monstrosities, the urban gated communities, and seem to add to the ghost town feeling of the night. I'm done for the night, pocket full of cash, eyes full of sand, time to head home. I make the turn onto Park and stop at the next light, the only car in view.

Wearily, I book out for the night and turn off my computer, then crack my knuckles. The light seems endless, no cars coming in any direction, alone in the night. I'm tempted to run the light, but wait it out, and make my way up Park. As I pass the Unsafeway, I see a flash of bright pink from my right and slow. There is Carrie, head down, bright hair like a beacon in the night. She leans with her shoulder against a tree, slowly walking in a circle around it. Like gravity has drawn her there, and is forcing her into a relentless orbit. Each turn bringing her lower and lower, towards the inevitable collision with the ground. I pull over and flip on my hazards, figuring I'll be fine with the lack of traffic. I get out, legs cramped and make my way over to the tree. I put my hand on her shoulder, and she looks up at me, groggily, then smiles. Her eyes are glazed and unfocused.

"'Sup, cowboy?"

"Come on, get in the cab." I hook my arm around her shoulders and put her arm around mine, then drag her towards the cab. She grins and mumbles something incoherent, as I lean her against the cab and open the passenger side door, and push the seat back. She has started to slide downward when I turn back to her. I manhandle her into the seat, reach over and put on her seatbelt, the carefully close the door. I run around to the driver's side and get in.

"Where we going, darlin'? Marion Street?" She's nodded off by this time, so I take her face in my hand and shake her gentle.

"Carrie, baby, wake up, where am I taking you?" Her eyes flutter, then focus on me, a grin comes to her face.

"Hi, Cowboy, what are you doing here?" I snort a short laugh.

"You were just about passed out in that park, where can I take you, Marion?"

"No, no," she slurs, "That's all fucked up, can't stay there, can't stay anywhere." She starts to cry. "No fucking where!" Suddenly she starts slamming her fists against the dashboard. "Everything is fucked, just fucked!"

I reach over and grab her hands.

"Easy, Carrie, easy." I pull her towards me, she leans against me, and I smell the jasmine smell, but now with a slightly sour undertone. "You sure? There's absolutely no place I can take you?"

She shakes her head, slightly over emphasized, swaying with each shake.

"Nope, no place, nowhere, no-thing. Just shit." She pauses for a moment, then looks up at me, a look of almost grotesque hope on her face. "How about your place, can I crash at your place?"

I hesitate and feel like a shit for it. It's not like I haven't fucked this girl, used her like she used me. But it seems like a line that's dangerous to cross, forbidden, or at least supremely dangerous territory. A change from business mixed with pleasure to…something else. A destruction of the hidden sanctuary of my house, a scary new level of our relationship, if I can call it that. I look at her hopeful face, mascara smeared and desperate, and know that I can't just leave her on the side of the road, alone with no place to go. At times like this I wish I was the jerk I try to be, with no sympathy for life's stray puppies and wounded souls. I sigh.

"Sure, Carrie, sure." I turn off the hazards and start back up Park, home to god knows what.

✿ ◉ ◎ ✿

She passes back out in the five blocks back to my house. I pull in front of my house, park in front of fire hydrant and toss on the hazards. Then wrestle Carrie out of the car and up my front steps, leaning her against the side of the house like a sack of groceries. I get the door open, then pull her inside while the screen door bangs against my back and dump her unceremoniously on the couch. I run back out and cruise around for parking. Ten minutes later, I'm creaking up my front steps and into my living room. She's slumped against the edge of the couch in what looks like an incredibly uncomfortable position. I sigh and wonder what the fuck I've gotten myself into as I lever her up off the couch and up the stairs into my room. I lay her on the bed, take her shoes off, and then wonder whether or not to take off her clothes, then decide against it, and toss a sheet over her. As an afterthought, I run downstairs and get a pan and set it next to her head on the floor. My room is a mess, but no need to add to the smell and garbage with a pile of girl puke. As I'm setting the pan down, her eyes open, slightly, and a dazed smile hits her lips.

"Hey."

"Hey, yourself," I say, trying to be gruff, "how ya feeling?"

"OK." She lifts herself up on one elbow and looks around the room. "so this is where the magic happens, eh, cowboy?" She gently sets herself down, resting her head on one hand and looks me square in the eye. "You gonna take advantage of me?"

I feel a stirring, but shake me head.

"No, baby, you're good here."

"Aww, you're no fun," her smile is weak and fading, I can tell she's going to nod off again.

"Yeah, I know, just an old curmudgeon, here's a pan if you have to puke, OK?"

"Sure, sure…thanks." Her eyes close and soon she's snoring gently. I stand up and stretch, contemplating the passed out girl in my bed, then shake my head slightly. Bemused, I turn off the light, and go downstairs to count my money.

I realize I had a pretty good night as I sip my scotch and sort the money into its various piles, then back into a big stack. I count a few times because my head is fuzzy and I keep coming up with different numbers. When I come up with the same amount three times in a row, I lean back and roll my head around, working out the kinks.

Finally I split the cash into two piles and contemplate where to put it. I feel like a jerk, but I just don't feel safe leaving all this cash lying around, or even in my pants with what amounts to a complete stranger in my house. I get up and pace around the living room, finally deciding to hide one half in a book on the bookshelf, and the other out back in an unused planter, then come back inside and sit down with my scotch.

I contemplate sleeping on my couch, but rebel against the idea. It's my fucking house, after all. Strange that it feels wrong to share a bed with her after fucking her. Like sleeping in the same bed is some higher level of intimacy that sticking my dick in her... Fuck it. I finish my drink, then go upstairs, strip down to my underwear, and slide into bed next to her. I roll over so my back is to her and listen to her soft breathing. The bed seems strangely constricted as I toss and turn, trying to get comfortable. I think of how it was when Mary first left. How the bed seemed like an immense empty field of mattress. Me still sleeping on my side of the bed for months, until I subconsciously moved slowly to the middle as I slept, sprawled out, arms and legs akimbo. Finally comfortable alone in bed, not waking up in the middle of the night when my half-awake arm flailed out to encounter emptiness and blank bed sheet, rather than warm flesh and comfort. Now I can't get to sleep because of the warm presence of another body in my bed. I roll over and make out the soft contour of her shoulder. It's bare except for the strap of her tank top, the soft fuzz at the nape of her neck, the indecipherable Chinese tattoo, and I feel a gentle sadness that seems to be everywhere with me these days. An hour or so later I finally drift off to a fitful sleep, dreaming of fields of rotten flowers and endless driving.

❋ ⊙ ◎ ❋

When I wake up, it's early afternoon sometime, and I lie there trying to focus for a few minutes. I remember taking Carrie home, and realize she isn't in the bed. Feeling a little self-conscious, I toss on my bathrobe and walk through the house. She's gone, not even a note. Guiltily, I take out my two piles of cash, and count them. It's all there and I feel more like shit. I shower quickly and dress, getting ready for Saturday, big money day. As I'm grabbing my keys I notice that my change jar is gone. I guess she took it. I feel a little betrayed but not all that angry, after all, she's in bad circumstances, and what is a jar full of change to me at this point anyway? Just a rainy day fund, maybe a twelver on a day off. Might mean much more for her. Still, makes me feel less like an asshole for hiding my cash. No need to be a totally easy target, right?

✿ ◉ ◉ ✿

I get a call from my suburban/Lodo regular around nine, and head out to Littleton to grab him, since that adds a guaranteed eighty or ninety bucks to my day. I may miss a few Cap Hill pick-ups, but I know I've got a big cash ending to my night, and that makes the night at little easier to deal with. Of course that means that there's no way in hell I'm calling it until I get that call to grab him at the end of the night. But it's Friday, my lease is almost paid off, and around midnight all I'll be doing is letting the cash roll in. Then tomorrow: Saturday, the one night a week where the fucking cab company doesn't get dime one from my tired and pathetic carcass. Maybe if tonight and tomorrow are good, I'll take Sunday off. That'd be the first day off in 17 days, and the thought is nice, but I know I'll at least spend a few hours sitting in the sun reading and getting some beer money together. At the very least. What's more likely is at least six hours in the cab, sweating Monday's fucking lease payment. I pop on I-25, gun it up to eighty, whip by the stadium. Fast lane all the way and fuck the cops. Windows rolled down, hat tucked under my leg, sweat cooling in the breeze, whooping it up, radio blaring. As I've said before, sometimes I just like driving.

✿ ◉ ◉ ✿

He's got a rowdy crew of tech geeks with him when I pull up, ready to try and meet "ladies of the female persuasion". Well, that leaves out a few bars I know of, anyway. We head back into town with no specific destination. They're chock full of misplaced tension and alcohol, laughing and shouting, just short of doing a round of high-fives. Obviously they've been doing some pregaming. As we get closer to downtown, I start pressing for a specific drop off, and they start quizzing me on local hot spots, where to meet girls, etc. Like I fucking know, all of my sexual experiences of the last year and a half have been in the fucking cab. Of course I don't tell them that. You share something like that with a customer, and they start looking real funny at the seats, and try not to touch anything too much. I feel bad for them, since all the seem to do is hit Lodo and strike out every time I take them downtown. So I suggest a Capitol Hill bar that I see good looking women outside of, but that I'd probably never set foot in, judging from the fares I'd picked up from there. They agree excitedly, pathetically happy to be out of their slim suburban comfort zone, and I hop off Santa Fe at Sixth and head happily away from downtown, into my comfort zone.

As I'm driving up sixth, it starts raining. One of those rare summer rains in Colorado, steaming up off of the hot streets, making things suddenly humid. We roll up the windows against the rain, and I fiddle with the air conditioning controls that I never use. The windows fog up, and I find myself wiping at the windshield, cracking my window, ignoring the drizzle drifting into my leg, and jokingly telling the guys to stop breathing. The wind kicks up, and suddenly the slight rain has turned into a full-fledged summer deluge. The rain is moving sideways, and I feel like we're in a submarine, as I quickly roll up my window, jeans soaked in a few seconds. We slow to a crawl, as I peer out of the cab, through layers of water. I pull over and shut the meter off.

"I think we're going to have to wait this one out, guys," I say as I watch the water run down the street and overflow the gutters.

"Holy shit," one of the guys mutters, and points to a fountain of water shooting out of a manhole.

I watch the rain blowing sideways across the street, look at the water raging down the street, over the sidewalks, the hammering din of rain and small hail pinging off my hood and roof, and remember a time in New Orleans in my youth. Full blown hurricane. Running screaming through the streets, drunk as hell. Before Katrina, dumb youth, full of anger and lust, like the kids in my back seat. I feel ancient and world weary, prop a foot up on the dashboard, and wish I smoked. It'd fit the fucking mood I'm in. Of course, I'd have to roll the window down, and get my jeans even more wet. Hell, at this point it almost looks like I've pissed my pants.

The rain starts faltering and I can actually see out of my windshield. The defroster is running cold and clammy, my windshield wipers swiping back and forth and showing wet street instead of bright lights through rock candy rain. I pop the meter back on and head back up Sixth. Carefully move around a crashed truck driven by some dumbass who doesn't understand hydroplaning, only thinks "TRUCK!" I cruise by a shop keeper frantically pushing water out his door with a squeegee. That's the good thing about Denver's deluges; the die out as quickly as they start.

I turn on Josephine, then up Colfax, and make to turn across Colfax. The rain has stopped now, and there is a small crowed outside of the bar stuck in a rundown old hooker hotel. Hipsters and tattooed young women stand outside smoking cigarettes and desperately trying to look cool.

One of my fares taps me on the shoulder as I turn across Colfax and into the parking lot, excited. "Damn, check out that one, good call, man." I look briefly as I turn, windows still fogged up, and don't see the car that just pulled out of a parking space and is racing towards me. I see him at the last moment and we both lay on the brakes. Too late, too late. There is a pissing crunch sound, and I know my night is fucked. I put it park, step out quickly and point to the hotel's parking lot, cursing under my breath. Shit. I park, and the other car follows me.

I run my fare's card and they tip well, offering condolences. I put off the other driver, a young business type, while the machine runs the bill, then call dispatch and tell them I've had a wreck. They ask if anyone is hurt, I say no, they say they'll call the police and to wait. I go back to cursing under my breath and walk around to the front of my car to check the damage. A slightly cracked bumper.

I walk over to the other car, apologize and tell the driver I didn't see him, then check out his car. Not bad, just a cracked headlight. Could've been worse. I go back to my cab and turn the computer off and wait. Now I think it'd be really great if I smoked, give me something to do, rather than lean against my cab and eyeball the other driver. Fuck, I didn't even see him, where the hell did he come from?

❀◉◎◉❀

Finally the cop shows up and we start filling out forms. The supervisor for the cab company shows up part way through this, just another cabbie with more experience who gets paid extra for these things. He takes a few pictures of the damage and shakes his head, I go back to cursing under my breath.

"Every time it fucking rains, man," he says to me, "every time. You're the fifth tonight." Great, don't I feel fucking special?

Once we fill out the accident report I follow the supervisor back to cab central, and we have the night dispatch buzz us upstairs. I sit in a room with the supervisor while I fill out yet more paper work, then turn in my keys. Had to happen on a fucking Saturday night. The supervisor tells me that I'm suspended until Monday and then have to come in and talk to one of the managers, who, of course are only available at 9 o'clock in the fucking morning. Makes me wonder, cab driving is a 24 hour deal, with most of the cash coming in at night, yet they run it like some nine to five business. No help for fucking cabbies, they just want their fucking money. Feeling bitter, I go to my cab and grab my personal stuff. The supervisor offers me a ride back to Capitol Hill, gratis, which is nice, since there's no way I want to spend the cash on a cab, especially with no more money coming in for the weekend.

We drive off, me in a deep funk, and he asks me where I want to be dropped. Fuck, I've got a Saturday off, might as well play it up like the normal folks do.

"Drop me at the Lair," I tell him. I haven't seen a local show in ages, maybe someone good is playing. Drinks are cheap, and I might not have to pay a cover, since I drive home several of the bartenders.

He gets a fare when we're about 10 blocks away, I tell him to go ahead and drop me, and he does, grateful. The rain has stopped completely and the deluge has cooled the scorching day off, leaving it comfortable and cool. I walk down Colfax, past rundown stores, restaurants and neon bars, avoiding spare changers, drug dealers, and drunk Lakota. I'm focused on a drink, music, maybe some female companionship. I pull out my phone, think, hell, why not, and call Jody. Better now than when I'm drunk.

"Hey," she answers, "what're you doing calling on a busy Saturday night?"

"Got in a wreck."

"Oh, no"

"Nothing bad, just have a surprise night off, wondering if you want to grab a drink. I'm heading over to the Lion's Lair. I know it's across town, but…"

"But you don't have a car to come to my neck of the woods."

"Exactly."

"Sounds like fun, I don't really have anything planned. Can't stay out too long, though… Who's playing?"

"No idea."

"Perfect. I'll see you in about a half an hour."

"Great." I find that I'm grinning ear to ear. Who knew? After the phone call I feel much better, almost like a normal person. A Friday night on the town, some music, some drinks, maybe a date? Not sure about the last one, but maybe. Having drinks with a woman instead of dirty sex in the front seat of my cab and dark blowjobs in back alleys. Who cares if I can't make my lease, my bills, my mortgage.

I sure as hell don't. Not quite whistling a jaunty tune, I walk down Colfax to the Lair, suddenly perversely happy that I wrecked my cab.

❀◉◉❀

The doorman is sitting on a barstool outside the door smoking a cigarette when I get there. I've driven him home a few times, mostly crippled drunk around 3:30 in the morning. I'm not sure if he'll recognize me.

"Hey, cab man, what's up? Who you picking up?" He starts to get up and head inside and I stop him.

"Not driving tonight, wrecked my cab about an hour ago."

"That sucks."

"You'd think so," I say and smile, "but now I get to swill beers and see a show on a Saturday night for once. What's the cover?" I reach in to my jeans, but he stops me with a wave.

"Don't worry about it, dude. You've picked me up wasted off my ass enough times I figure I owe ya, go on in."

I thank him and head into the grungy bar. It's dark and the band is fairly deafening. On my way to the bar I look around to see if I know anyone and come up blank. Everyone is about ten years younger than me. I was hoping to see one or two old friends, but I figure they're all married and living the good life in the suburbs, like I probably should be. I elbow my way to the bar and wave a twenty, trying to get the bartender's attention. She serves a few people before she sees me, then smiles and comes over.

"You're not working?" She yells over the din. I shake my head and point at a beer tap. She nods, pours me a beer, and then waves me off when I try to pay. Damn, I should wreck my cab more often. I toss two bucks down for a tip and squirm my way away from the bar. The place is packed, hot and damp. I drink my beer quickly, then check my phone as I head back to the bar, see how long it's been since I called Jody. I order another beer, pay this time and watch the band for a bit. I feel my phone vibrate in my pocket, so I slam my beer, set it down and walk outside, pulling my phone out.

"Hi," I say cheerfully, thinking it's Jody.

"Hey, cowboy," the voice is slurred and quiet, "come get me." Shit, of course she'd call now.

"Sorry, Carrie, darlin'. Wrecked my cab, I'm not working."

"Oh," there is a pause, "where are you, I can come and hang out."

"I'm at a bar," shit, wouldn't that be great?

"Oh, damn, I don't have a fake ID. I'm only nineteen, you know that, right?"

"Yeah, I know, I think you told me at some point." She didn't but I'd figured.

"Well, um, maybe we can hang out a little later." She sounds wasted and I feel like a dick for thinking that she just wants a place to crash, namely my place.

"Sure, sure," I say, "Call me later," hoping she won't. I look down the street and see Jody walking up in a yellow and white sundress, hair pulled back into French braids, looking like fine a summer morning, and I need to hang up.

"Ok…" I hang up as she walks up.

"Anything important?" She asks nodding to my phone.

"No, no I guess not, just a regular needing a ride that I can't give." Ain't that the truth.

She smiles and takes my arm.

"What a shame," she says as we walk back into the bar, the doorman bowing low, arm outstretched towards its dark interior, like some punk rock bell hop ushering us into the best of establishments.

✿ ◎ ◉ ◎ ✿

The band is blasting loud, making conversation almost impossible, but it makes my blood rise to hear loud music in a crowded bar with a woman. I'd forgotten how much I missed a good Saturday out on the town. We thread our way to the bar and I order us a couple of drinks. We head to the back of the bar so we can see the band without getting pushed around or stomped on. They're good, not great, but good. The night goes on like that, me drinking two for her one, leaning against the back wall, heads nodding to the beat. A far cry from my old days bleeding and sloshing beer in the pit, but probably better for a night with Jody. Less frenetic a little more adult. We talk a bit between bands, about nothing at all. Then the time comes when she has to go, after the second band and before the headliner. I walk her to the car, a little unsteady on my whiskey sea legs, beaming and high. When we get to her car, we stop, in the classic awkward moment.

"You good to drive?" I ask, a little sloppy, pointing at her car. "I mean, my place is close…"

"No, no I'm good." She says a little too quickly, or so I think.

"Oh," I stutter, "I mean I've got an extra room, or I can sleep on the couch, or…" I'm out of options except for the one I want, her in my bed. Maybe not even sex, just a warm body to drape an arm over. She smiles and stops me with a hand on the cheek.

"It's OK, I'm fine, and I do have to get up early. You seem like you're just getting started."

"Well," I reply, not sure how to take that, "I am on a cabbie's schedule." Did that come out too defensive? Fuck, I was messing this up. Too over eager, like a horny Yorkie humping her leg.

"I know, don't worry about it."

"Maybe we could do this again," I find myself blurting out. Fuck, here I go, humping away at that tanned leg of hers.

"Sure," she smiles and opened her car door, "maybe with a little more planning."

"Yeah," I find myself saying as she turns to her car, "I had a good time."

"Yeah," she turns back, "me too."

I half stumble half lunge for a kiss, Christ what a fucktard, I think, as she turns her cheek and I half-kiss, half-slobber on her cheek. Well, that let her know where I stand, and left me completely in the dark as to how she stood. Nice move. She smiles, pats me on the cheek and gets into the car.

"Bye, I'll talk to you soon." She starts the car up, and, rather than stand there, blank-eyed, drunk, and idiotic, to and watch her drive off, I wave and head back to the bar. It's going to take quite a few drinks to wipe the smell of that epic screw up off of me.

❀◉◉❀

I wake up on my couch, face pressed into the fabric, one arm trailing off on the floor, the other numb and tangled under me. Boots on, knees bent up, muscles knotted. For a moment, I'm not sure where I am, then I roll over and off the couch, onto the floor. Hard. I stand up unsteadily and head to the kitchen for some water to replace the sands of the Sahara that have blown into my mouth while I slept. As I'm leaned over the sink, throwing water on my face, the debacle of the night before hits me. First thing even approaching a real date since the divorce, and I come across drunk and desperate.

I sit at my kitchen table, drink more water, and try to analyze the entire encounter by her car. In the end not too bad a faux pas, just a little drink and grope attempt, and she said she wanted to go out again, this time with some planning. Now the question was whether to call her or not. If I called right away, I'd seem desperate, which was no secret after last night. If I waited a day or two, then I'd seem embarrassed or scared. Better desperate than wimpy, I decide, and call her up. I get her message, and decide to try to play it cool.

"Hey, had a good time last night, wouldn't mind doing it again, maybe in a week or so, once I get my cab stuff sorted out after the accident. Give me call."

Not too bad, the old "pretend it didn't happen" gambit that I seemed to recall from my dating days oh, so many years ago. I make coffee and wonder why it couldn't just be simple: I like you, you like me, let's get naked. Of course, when it did work that way, it was still hopelessly complicated. Look at Carrie, fun in a real dirty kind of way, but complicated. She always wanted something from me and seemed to pay for it with sex, whether it was watching her back, giving her a place to crash, or just plain money. I pour my coffee, sit back down at the table, and decide to put it all aside and figure out what to do with a couple of days off. I find I have no idea what to do. What did people do with days off? I could mow the lawn, do the dishes, watch TV? Of course the big temptation is to get good and day drunk. Go grab lunch and a screwdriver at some local bar, and then go and wile the day away on some patio with a pitcher of margaritas or a cold beer. A good serious fuck all day. Then again, bills are due, my lawn is overgrown, and who knows when I can get back into the cab and make some money. I should be productive, but I'm not sure what the hell that means any more. Paralyzed with indecision, I sit at the table and drink my coffee.

I could do something creative, play my guitar…masturbate? Play my guitar while masturbating? Deep down I know that I'm just prolonging the inevitable; a dark bar and a cold beer. I finish off my coffee, put the cup in the sink with the dirty dishes, grab my sunglasses, and head out the door to the nearest bar.

✿◉◉✿

Walking down the street in the blazing sun, I realize that I'm still kind of drunk from the night before. That kind of feeling where you can feel the brutal blazing eyes of the hangover glaring in from the darkness at the edge of the campfire. Primitive and primordial with sharp teeth, wicked claws, and with a headache like being clubbed with a rock. Sometimes the only way to stop a serious maiming is to put more wood on the fire until it blazes high and shatters the night, chasing away the demons of the dark. For now, anyway. In simpler terms, I need to get loaded before my hangover hits me, so I can put it off for one more day. As the sun beats into me, I begin to realize that I'm also horrible dehydrated. My mouth is dry, I'm slightly dizzy, and my fingers feel like they're swelling up like plump cooked sausages. I know now that I need strong drinks, lots of water, and some food. By the time I make it to the nearest bar that fits the bill I begin to feel that dogged edge of sobriety.

When I walk in to the bar, I can almost sense the day regulars recoiling from the light of the sun burning in through the open door. I quickly close it, and stand there letting my eyes adjust to the dark. There's several chairs open at the bar and I pick one isolated and at the end of the bar. I don't recognize the bartender when she comes up, which is just as well, I suppose, considering the bartenders I know tend to try to kill me with kindness by serious amounts of over pouring.

I order a breakfast burrito, a glass of water and a screwdriver, and quickly down the water, motioning for another, and drinking most of that before I hit the screwdriver. The orange juice, if that's what it is, is a bit too sweet, but thinned out nicely by a copious and almost criminal amount of vodka. Maybe I do know the bartender. Either way, bless her black heart and leaden pour hand. I'm starting in on my fifth glass of water and third screwdriver when the burrito arrives, a brutal and obscene creation stuffed with three kinds of breakfast meat, eggs, and potatoes, and smothered in chunky pork green chili and cheese. A veritable heart attack on a plate. I dig in and soon find myself surprised that I finished the whole damn thing off. I feel the food kicking in, countermanding the booze, and quickly order another to maintain the precarious balance between hangover and plastered.

On my fifth screwdriver I give up any pretense of hydration and put it off to for another time and realm. Now is the booze time, I think, now is the fading afternoon, the quiet at the bar, the success after the hunt. I relax into the bar, watching TV and breathe a sigh of relief. So this is what it's like to have a day off, to have a fucking weekend. I love it. Maybe I won't go to that damn meeting on Monday, and just tell them to go take a flying fuck. I can sell the damn house and live off it for a while, just wile away the days at the bar. Then I remember child support, bills, and how long it'll take to sell the damn place, and realize with brutal clarity, that I'm stuck behind that damn wheel. That I need those fuckers, and that there's no way out of the grind, just work, pay bills, and go back to work, ad infinitum, until I die in the harness. Fuck. The whole thought of it makes me feel sick and tired of life. I sigh and order another cocktail. At least I have this. I have the now, right? This quiet moment in a bar, solitude in public and a cold drink. There's some solace in this dismal world, at least.

As I'm thinking these dark soul sucking thoughts and trying to buck myself up, a man sits next to me and orders a beer. He's a tall, fairly burly guy with a shaved head and glasses. He gets his beer takes a large quaff and nods to me, I nod back unsteadily.

"How, ya doing?"

"All right," I reply warily, "and you?"

"Oh, fine, fine, mighty fine indeed, as Descartes," and he pronounces it like it's spelled- dez carts, for fuck sakes, "once said- 'work is the curse of the drinking classes'"

"Um, I don't think that was Descartes," I try, mustering myself up the challenge, "in fact I'm pretty sure it was..."

"No, no, I'm positive, it was Descartes."

"No, I'm pretty sure it was Oscar Wilde, now if you would have said- 'I drink therefore I am-'" I start, and he cuts me off.

"Descartes, my man. I read it." Like claiming to read it would give his madness credence. He starts on about Descartes' philosophy, which, as far as I can tell he thinks involves nihilism, drinking, and the "opium poppy". This then leads into a rather incoherent but self possessed version of the history of the opium wars. I find myself overwhelmed by his barrage of half-truths, misunderstood history, and mad ramblings. Every time I try to correct, interrupt, or add to the one way conversation, I'm overridden by polite condescension, and plenty of "no no, I assure you, my good man". I'm overpowered by his combination of ignorance, misplaced self-confidence, and verbal diarrhea as he blathers on and on. Finally, I feel something snap and I grab him by his shirt front and yell into his face, feeling spittle flying from my mouth to spatter on his glasses.

"Would you shut up you fucking pompous windbag!" I feel a year of anger and frustration boiling out of me, and I feel the unholy desire to beat the snot out of this horrible barstool philosophizer. He blinks at me for a moment and I come to my senses and realize a hush has fallen over the bar. All the derelicts, hung over skateboarders, and day laborers are staring at me, fairly open mouthed. I release him slowly shaking slightly.

"Well, that was uncalled for, my good man," he says hurt and offended while he adjusts his shirt. I'm suddenly filled with the urge to punch him again, when the bartender comes up with my bill.

"No fights, pay up and get out." Great, I just want a nice peaceful day and I have to have the most amazing boor sit next to me and ruin it. Fine, there are other bars. I toss some cash on the bar and turn to leave.

"And it's pronounce 'day cart', he's French, you unholy bastard," I say, wagging my finger at him as I leave the bar. He cringes back slightly and starts cleaning my spit off his glasses. I shake my head, give the bar the finger, then leave. Well, don't think I'll be coming in there during the day any time soon. As I walk down Colfax back towards my house, I feel laughter bubbling up inside of me. What the fuck was that? My god, how does anyone put up with that ignorant know it all? I stop and lean against a building laughing, wiping tears from my eyes, and feel strangely sorry for the guy. He tries, and he's probably so damn lonely, which is why he tries and chats strangers up at bars with his own form of madness, poor guy. Still, I wouldn't want him sitting next to me at a bar, or, god forbid, on an airplane. They'd have to have the sky marshal truss me up like a fucking Christmas pig. Feeling ruined for bars for the rest of the day, I head to the liquor store and decide to spend the rest of the day doing chores and some good old fashioned porch drinking.

❀ ◉ ◉ ❀

I walk into the liquor store, the stuffy heat hitting me like a wave. Apparently their air conditioning is out. I wander the aisles scanning the labels, trying to decide what a good summer porch drink would be. I'm sick to hell of beer, and I started on vodka, so it might be good to continue the trend since going off reservation and mixing my liquors might have dire consequences. I look at the bottle of vodka for a while, contemplating, then do the asshole move and grab a fifth of rum and some daiquiri mix. Girl drinks it is. I'll have to dig out my blender, but what the hell, the blistering heat requires a solid counter argument. I walk up to the counter and set the bottles down.

"Hey, cab man," the little old Korean woman who owns the place beams at me, "you have day off?"

"Yep."

"Well, you have fun, don't drink all of bottle."

"You got it," I smile and wave and make my way out of the store. Days off are good, I decide as I head home.

The blender is buried behind a food processor and some cookie pans, but for the life of me I can't find the lid for the damn thing. I pour equal parts mix and rum over ice and hit blend, spraying pink liquid up and onto the counter. Cursing, I find a small plate, and hold it over the top while it blends. It prevents the contents of the blender from splattering all over the kitchen, but it still drips a steady stream of pink goo down the side of the blender. In a vindictive mood I might assume that Mary took the top of the blender, like she took the sheets. More passive aggressive bullshit, I mutter, turn off the blender, wash my hands, and pour myself a glass of sticky sweet rum cocktail. I sip it and grimace at the strength and sweetness of the drink, but I have to admit that it is quite refreshing. I go out on the porch, sit and watch the traffic go by as I sip my girlie drink. The yard is overgrown and full of garbage, and I decide it's high time I mowed the damn lawn.

I go upstairs and rummage through my laundry until I find the one pair of shorts I own- plaid, probably a joke buy for a costume party or something. I can't quite remember. I change into them, and, looking at myself in the mirror, wish I had a pair of sandals, black socks and sock garters. My legs are the pasty pasty white of skin that hasn't seen the sun in years, the plaid shorts fit badly, and don't quite go with the slight paunch, black t-shirt and cowboy hat. I find an old pair of combat boots and put them on to complete the ensemble. Now it's definitely some sort of drunken summer yard work dress up party.

I finish of the daiquiri, go down stairs and pour the rest of the blender into my drink, and head out to the shed in my back yard. I pull out the crappy old lawn mower that I got at a yard sale a few years back, and start drunkenly yanking at the cord. After about five tries, wheezing, I pick my drink back up and take a pull. Heart beating heavily, I imagine the coroner's mirth when they pull my pasty bloated clown-dressed corpse out of the shed. I take a sip, sit down and wonder what the hell I do. I could check the spark plugs, but all that would tell me is whether or not the damn thing has spark plugs.

I check the gas tank, and find it mostly empty. I set my drink back down and rummage through the shed until I find a half empty gas can, and fill up the tank. It starts on the third pull, and I'm left with the quandary of how to push the lawn mower while holding my drink in my hand. I try it for a bit, but seem to list to the right a bit too much, almost like I'm going in a circle. Resigned, I put my drink on the back steps and start mowing. I hit the first clump of grass almost at running speed and the engine chokes and dies. I pull it back and yank on the cord, starting it back up. Slow and easy, I think as I go to the stairs and take a drink. I go back to the mower and ease it forward slowly, pulling it back as it starts to choke. Fuck, this is going to take forever I think, as I head back to the porch. Lawn work is thirsty business. I find I can go a decent pace where the grass is dried up and dying, and don't bother to move any but the largest trash. Thus I'm spraying bits of plastic bags, Styrofoam, and toys the neighbors kids have thrown over the fence all over the lawn. I don't really care, I just want to get the grass cut before it becomes a jungle.

I finish the back yard about the same time I finish my drink, and push the mower around to the front. Time for a break, I decide, and go into the kitchen to mix up another batch of blender drinks. I sit on the porch and finish another blender full, then mix up a third. I notice, kind of blurry like, that there isn't much of the bottle left. I'm weaving quite a bit at this point, but now I'm on a fucking mission. I start the lawn mower back up and start careening around the front yard with the mower, trying to make good orderly rows.

I wake up around eight at night, sun going down, combat boots stretched in front of me, breeze blowing across my shins, sun burnt and stinging from being battered with tiny plastic bits, drink in my hand, flopped down in a chair on my porch. Groggily I sit up, and look at my lawn. It looks like a gardener's nightmare: Bits of grass sticking up between unsteady mulch-clogged rows. It's about three quarters done, with the lawn mower rammed into a particularly tall batch of grass. I wonder what passing cars thought of my bizarre appearance: Combat boots, Bermuda shorts and a cowboy hat. I touch my face and feel the tenderness and heat of a serious sunburn. Fuck it, I think and stumble inside and to bed.

❀ ◉ ◎ ❀

Monday rolls around too soon, and not soon enough. When I pull my phone out I have 15 messages, all but 14 from regulars wanting a ride. A crappy reminder of how much money I lost over the weekend, my hangover being a fairly brutal reminder of how much money I spent. The one message that isn't from a regular is from Jodi which might and might not make the weekend worthwhile. I wonder if it's going to be good or bad news, then check my messages. I rapidly erase the drunken "where are you?" messages, and finally get to hers:

"Hey, I had a good time, too. Sure we can do it again, maybe in a few weeks, my school and work schedule is hell right now..." she pauses, "um, sorry I seemed a bit stand offish, I just, well, it's been awhile since I went out, and, uh, oh, I don't know, things are still confusing, let's just take it slow and see what happens," she ends the sentence with a questioning emphasis, and I'm not sure what to make of it. "Well, ah, crap, call me next week sometime, OK?"

Good news? Bad news? Hell I don't know. I save the message to brood over at some other time and catch a bus out to the cab yard for my joyous moment in the principal's office. I get there on time, but they make me wait an extra fifteen minutes. With the mood I'm in, I feel for sure that it's some kind of power trip to establish their dominance and place me off guard. Probably out of some middle management self-help book titled something like "I'm OK, You're Insignificant: A Middle Management Guide to Brow-Beating Your Way to the Top"

When I come in the day manager is sitting, bloated and pasty, behind his desk, while some lady from HR is leaning against a file cabinet. Great, we going to play good cop bad cop too?

I sit down and the fat manager flips through my file silently for a moment, and I'm not sure if I want to call him a fat fuck or laugh my ass off at his fake seriousness. He looks up at me.

"So, is this your first wreck?" I know it's in my file, and wonder why the fuck he's asking.

"No, two others, both not my fault, both getting rear-ended by soccer moms."

"So, this is the first one that was you're fault?" What the fuck did I just say?

"Yep."

"Run me through the accident." I sigh, and walk him through it. Raining, didn't see the guy, minor fender bender, no one hurt, two scraped bumpers, what's the big deal? He sits for a moment, then closes my file.

"Well, we're going to let you keep driving." Fucking whoopee. "But, you have to retake the driver safety course, and your insurance payments are going up for a year." I was wondering when they'd get to the money.

"How much?"

"Let's see..." he pulls another piece of paper towards him, "looks like your lease is going to go up seventy three dollars a week."

"Fine," I don't see what kind of choice I have, it's take it or quit. "Are you going to prorate my lease for last week?" He smiles broadly, we're all friends here. We're corn holing you nice and good, what's a little reach around between friends?

"Sure, we'll take off let's see... one and a half days."

"But I'll be off for two and a half."

"Yes, but Sundays are free, so we'll just give you today, and half of Saturday." In other words: I'm being nice, but I'm still fucking you.

"Whatever," I say wearily, and he looks offended, like I should be hugging the bastard for the chance to work, "when's the class?"

He signs me up for eight o'clock the next morning. Of course they don't have any afternoon classes, I sign some paperwork, and leave with a bad taste in my mouth. On the bus back to my place I do the math. The accident is going to cost me nearly four grand over the next year. Fuck, I could have replaced both bumpers for under a grand. Why the fuck am I paying for insurance? I'm beginning to understand how miners felt when they went to the company store. Bastards.

❀ ◉ ◎ ❀

I'm there bright and early the next morning, eye's gummed with sleep, with a big cup of coffee in my hand. I remember the class from the prior year, mostly a series of badly produced corporate films, and a lecture on not being a moron. I'm not disappointed:

DEATH ON THE STREETS:
OR DON'T DRIVE LIKE AN ASSHOLE

FADE IN: EXT. SNOWY STREET — DAY

Montage of cars swerving through snow laden

intersections, mixed with cars stuck with
tires spinning.

ANNOUNCER

Death on the streets! This could be you!
Remember, driving in snow is different
than driving on the street. Always pump
your breaks! Or the next death… could be
yours!

✿◉◎✿

I'm out taking a breath of fresh air on our break, the air conditioning in the building being subarctic. Apparently all of the extra blubber on the office staff has advantages. Me, I wish I'd brought a jacket. Standing next to me is a swarthy cab driver, middle eastern, maybe Egyptian, smoking a cigarette. He offers me one, and I wave him off.

"Fucking class," he mutters in a heavily accented voice, "I know how to drive, I'm from fucking Cairo. I'd like to see one of those fuckers drive in that traffic. But, no, I have to sit through fucking video telling me to look in my fucking mirrors." He shakes his head. "Sure we have no snow in Egypt, but still, just don't drive like asshole, right?"

He looks at me, and I snort in agreement.

"Hands at ten and two," he says in a mocking voice, holding his hands out like he's driving. He snorts, shakes his head and takes a deep drag off of his cigarette. "I feel like they think that I am fucking ten and two." I laugh and he looks over at me. "What are you in for?"

"It was raining, my fare was distracting me, and I didn't see the guy pull out," I shrug, "Fuck, you drive 70 hours a fucking week, and it's bound to happen eventually."

"You only drive 70 hours?" He laughs. "But, true. Bound to happen, and when it does? They act surprised and treat you like retarded child."

"And raise your lease payments."

"Yes, and fuck you for more money... bastards. We should start our own fucking company."

"Good luck on that, they got the P.U.C. pretty tied up."

"True, true, but it would be worth it to tell them to go to hell."

He grinds his cigarette out and we head back inside.

❀ ⊙ ⊙ ❀

Another couple of hours and some more bad film later, I sit in the over air conditioned driver's room and wait for my cab. They might have one ready, they might not. Basically, I'm waiting for one of two things to happen: a driver getting fed up and turning in their keys or a car that's been in an accident after it's been fixed and cleared for driving to be released. You always hope for the driver quitting because that way you have a better chance of a cab that hasn't been through the wringer, or that, perhaps, isn't made from three other cabs.

I sit, with my head down, trying to sleep. I saw that there were four names on the list before mine, so it's quite possible that I'll be here all day and not get a cab. The first time I waited for 6 hours before one came up, and I heard horror stories about cabbies waiting three or four days before one came up. This time I'm lucky and only have to wait three hours.

They call my name, hand me the keys and tell me to give it a once over. I walk outside, find the cab with the same number as the keys, open it up, get in and start it up. It starts on the first turn which is a good sign, I suppose. It has over three hundred thousand miles, but has vinyl seats, which is a plus when you get pukers, just squeegee and drive. I look at the gas gage and am amazed to find over half a tank of gas. Must've been a newbie who either quit, wrecked, or broke down. I get out and do a walk around, pop the trunk, check for damage. The paint seems a bit worn, but it's probably actually better than my last cab. Of course, I have no idea what I'd do if it was a huge P.O.S.

It's not like I could afford to turn it down, I'm out of cash, owe a lot on my lease, and need to get back on the road and pay some damn bills.

I turn it off and go inside to sign off on the cab. Then I wait for the computer to come on and recognize me as I drive back to my house to pick up my cab stuff. It takes until I'm almost home to book in. It's one in the afternoon on a Tuesday, and I know I'll be busting ass until four in the morning. I park in the no parking zone in front of my house, book in to 111, then run in to take a piss and grab my stuff. The computer's blinking by the time I get back, and I accept the bell just in time.

It's one zone over, but I don't mind, I feel the need to get rolling and drive, hoping like hell that Tuesday will be a good fucking day for a chance. The worst part of the experience is that I might have lost several regulars who called when I wasn't driving. I send out a mass text when I'm sitting at stop lights trying to make it to Cherry Creek Mall. It's a pretty standard day fare, a Midwestern couple visiting from Iowa, staying at hotel downtown, and doing some shopping. The talk is bland and inane, but decent money, a good start. I drop them downtown, think, like I always do, that I might wait in the cab line in front of a hotel, then just head downtown and head for Cap Hill. I get a bell right away for the Botanic Gardens, and head up to York, another tourist bell. I begin to wonder if I shouldn't drive earlier on week days.

As I'm driving, there's a little panicked voice in the back of my head rambling on and on about numbers, bills obligations. The mortgage, child support, my lease, overdue student loans, a crushing weight added to the stress of driving, dealing with drunks, keeping a friendly demeanor, all hell and high water, overwhelming. I think back to my twenties and how losing a job meant nothing. I'd figure I'd find a job or not. If not, I'd figure something out, maybe drift around the country with my backpack as my companion, working here and there, doing whatever. It was never a big deal, I had nothing to lose. Being poor when you're young is beauty and freedom, you don't mind losing because you have nothing to lose. Being poor and old is a sin, a giant smashing shit hammer of burden and stress. I could lose the house, I had already lost wife and child and self-respect. Lose the job and I'd lose the house, miss my child support and end up in jail. It would almost be a relief to just give every goddamn thing up and go live under a bridge. Or keep driving and see how long it took the cab company to find me. Just drive until I hit the sea, then pile out and start swimming till the cold waters of the ocean swallowed me up, and spit my white bloated fish eaten corpse up on the beach.

With these glorious thoughts rebounding in my head, I make make my way to what they are calling "Uptown" now. When I lived there it was just part of Five Points. Now that it's mostly white, they have to rename it so it isn't associated with the "bad" part of town.

When I take time to look at the actual address for the bell, I see that it's for the grocery store in Uptown that Denverites just call the Unsafeway. Great, a grocery run. Grocery runs are notorious for low or no tip. Nothing like a short run no tip fare with the added glory of hauling groceries. I think the only time I got a decent tip on a grocery run was on my training day and the cabbie who was training me got to keep that. I sigh and keep driving, though not with nearly as much enthusiasm. It's a roll of the dice, et cetera et cetera. It's just that lately it was feeling like the dice were loaded and I was only rolling snake eyes.

I pull into the parking lot and am waived down by a large angry looking black woman behind a shopping cart stuffed to overflowing with groceries. I pop the hood, get out and start loading groceries, I wasn't expecting a tip, but it never hurts to try.

What took you so damn long?" She starts tearing into me almost as soon as I get out of the cab.

"I just got the call ma'am," I say, trying to placate her as I lift several twelve packs of soda into the trunk, "there might have been no one in the zone when you called."

"Well, I been waiting a half an hour," she huffed as she watched me load the groceries, "got some frozen stuff in there."

"I got here as quick as I could, ma'am."

"Humph, no, no," she slaps my hand away, "don't put that on the bottom, there's eggs in there." With a mighty effort, I restrain myself from telling her to load her own fucking groceries. The last thing I need is a customer complaint right after the wreck. They'd probably start charging me a twenty buck a day 'politeness surcharge". I manage to load the rest of the groceries correctly and hold the door open for her as she lowers her bulk diffidently into the back seat.

I get her address, a place about ten blocks away, and start to pull out of the parking lot.

"You already got the meter running?" Great, just great.

"Yes ma'am, once I pull up, it starts running."

She makes another harrumph noise and leans back in the seat.

We drive the rest of the ten blocks in stony silence and I pull into an alley behind a rundown section 8 apartment building. The fare is $7.40, she hands me a hundred dollar bill and I stifle a groan.

"I'll see if I can break that," I say as I pull wadded bills out from my pocket. I barely have enough and count it out for her. I place the last bill in her hand and she says nothing, hand still out. I turn and look at her as the moment stretches and she doesn't get out of the cab. She glares at me.

"Where's the sixty cents?" She thrusts her hand at me. I might have it in the ashtray, but damned if I'm going to go digging, finally I lose it.

"You have got to be fucking kidding!"

"Don't you curse at me!"

"Well, I don't carry change, lady, so deal with it." I pop the trunk and get out. She struggles out of the cab and by the time she gets out, I have half of her groceries unloaded and on the ground.

"It's stealing!" She shouts at me.

"It's sixty goddamn cents, lady, and I don't have it."

"Well, give me a dollar then."

"Hell no," I plop the last bag unceremoniously on the alley ground, slam the trunk and walk back to the driver's side door.

"You're rude!"

"And you're cheap, lady," I say, no longer caring about a write-up. I get in the cab and drive away as she screams at me.

About twenty minutes later I get a note on my computer to call the supervisor. Cursing under my breath I pull over and call in. Dispatch patches me into the supervisor and he starts to ream me out and I stop him.

"Look, the lady paid with a hundred and wanted exact change, do you hear me? Exact, as in to the penny. I don't have any change in my cab, and she lost it and became abusive, I did my best, but I can only put up with so much."

"Wait, this is over sixty cents?"

"Yeah."

"Man," he laughs, "sounds like a sweetheart."

"Yeah, a wonderful woman.'

"Ok, I understand, just try to have a more relaxed day, alright?"

"Will do." He hangs up and I shake my head and pull back out into traffic. I guess that sometimes management is on the driver's side... sometimes.

The day goes well, sliding into the night, but I can't seem to shake the irritation from the grocery run. I find that I'm being short and a bit surly to my rides, and my tips show it. I'd love to stop and get my head straight, but the loss from my days off is weighing heavily. That and the increase in my lease. I feel the pressure like a real thing, right between my shoulder blades. I pull over to stretch and I get a bell in Capitol Hill. Always seems like when you want a little down time the job won't let you, and when you're desperate for work you have all the time in the world. Grumpily, I take the bell and head over to Fourteenth. Amazingly, I find a parking space in front of the bar so I don't have to block traffic. I pull in, press the call back button and get out to stretch. My fare comes out of the bar and I bark out a laugh as I see the thin man in the nice suit, with his tie loosened rakishly.

"Well, I'll be damned," I say smiling, "if it isn't the devil himself."

He looks up from his cell phone and laughs.

"Dude! Well, fuck me, you're driving a cab?"

"No, stole it." I walk around the cab and give him a hug and pat on the back. "How the hell are you doing, Brad?"

"Great, man, great," he leans back and smiles, looking me in the eye. "You?"

"Eh," I shrug, not wanting to get into the twisted details of my life, "I'm doing." I motion to the cab. "Your chariot awaits, hop in." He nods and gets in the passenger seat, unceremoniously tossing my stuff in the back. I shake my head and go around to get in.

I met Brad back when I played in a band and lived with a bunch of degenerates in a ramshackle row house on the edge of Five Points. He was dating the next door neighbor, but seemed to spend more time over at our place drinking than hanging out with her. In the end, she dumped him, but he kept coming around to our place to booze it up. We'd stay up all night drinking, listening to Eighties punk and breaking things, then head out to the bum bars for a morning drink. He was a riot, and we had some epic drinking bouts. It was good to see him.

"Nice suit."

"Nice hat, you been going to Charlie's?" Charlie's was a gay cowboy bar on Colfax

"Hey," I said in mock seriousness, "they pour a strong drink there."

"That they do, that they do," he smiled and shook his head. "Man, it's good to see you."

"You too, Brad, you too. Where we going?"

"I don't know, where do you want to grab a drink?"

"I can't man, I gotta work, bills and such."

"Fuck that, I'll buy. Hell," he pulled out the lapels of his suit and tried to look dignified, "I'm a fucking corporate head hunter these days, I make a shitload of cash."

"You're shitting me. A head hunter?"

"You know it. I'm a fucking suit, dude." He laughs wildly, and I can tell he's already had a few.

"I can't, I need to make money." The temptation is overwhelming.

"What do you make a night, one hundred, two hundred?"

"Something like that," I say uncomfortably.

"Fuck it, I got that in my wallet."

"I'm not taking your money, Brad."

"I understand, I understand," he says sadly, "take me to that bar by the post office on Marion."

"Sure," I put the car in gear, "maybe another time.'

"Yeah,' he says, a hint of mischief in his voice. I look over and he has his wallet out. He takes a twenty out, balls it up and throws it over his shoulder. "Oops, dropped that fucker." He pulls out two more twenties, rolls them up and flings them about the cab.

"Cut it out Brad." A twenty bounces off my head and falls to floor by the gas pedal.

"Sorry, man, I'm just so bad with money." He giggles and drops another twenty on the floor.

"All right, all right, I'll come have a drink with you, you fucking maniac."

"A drink? One drink? What happened to you, you pussy?"

"Fine," I say laughing, "let's get fucking tanked."

"There you go, that's my buddy."

I drop him at the bar, then run home to drop the cab. I crawl around the cab finding five balled up twenties, and another couple jammed in the passenger seat. I vow to myself to give them back to him. But, knowing Brad, I think I might just lose that argument. I run into the house, hose myself off a bit, check my rumpled reflection in the mirror, shrug and start walking to the bar.

When I get to the bar, he has mostly empty drink and an empty shot glass in front of him.

"So," I say, eyeing the shot glass, "it's going to be one of those nights, huh?"

"You know it," he replies with a wicked smile and waives the bartender over. "Barkeep, get my friend here a drink and us two shots of bourbon." The bartender, a tattooed man with massive muttonchops nods and pours the shots. I order a beer and turn to toast Brad.

"Good to see you."

"And you." We down the bourbon, and he spins the glass on the bar, then looks at me. "What the hell are you doing driving a cab? Last I heard you were selling insurance, and making good money."

I shrug and tell him the whole story, leaving out the parts about the basement and the noose.

"Well, that's a bitch, but, man, you're a smart fucker, you could be doing anything." He reached into his wallet and pulls out his card. "Call, me, Ok? I'm pretty sure I can find you something."

I take the card, wondering if I'll take him up on it. I finish my beer and order another, and we do another round of shots.

"What's it like driving a cab? I bet you have some crazy stories."

I laugh and start telling him, and soon, it's all coming out; Carrie, Jody, the midgets, the madness and sorrow, the crying cab, everything. Many drinks later, we're both leaning into the bar heavily. Last call is rolling up, and, against better judgment, we order more shots.

"A nineteen year old stripper?" He slurs, pointing at me with his drink. "Guess you still got it, fucker."

"If I ever had it."

"Yeah," he looks down at the bar, suddenly maudlin. "Man, at least what you're doing is interesting. I deal with these suits all day. Fucking drones. Boring fucks one and all. Talking about sports, their new fucking lawn mower, whose garage is bigger, whose car is nicer. God, makes me wanna puke. But there I am, finding the best jerkoff for the job." He shrugs and takes a deep pull off of his beer. "It's a living. I've got it all, right? Big house, pretty wife, a kid on the way, nice car." He pauses, running his finger through the condensation on the bar, then looks up at me plaintively. "Am I a sell out?"

"No," I grab his shoulder and sway a bit. "No, you're, you're good man. You're successful. I mean, look at me: driving a fucking cab seventy hours a week, mortgage overdue, I chased away my wife and kid. Hell, I'm a fuck up, Brad, a total fuck up."

"No, no," he shakes his head vigorously and almost falls off the barstool. "We all go through shit times. This is just a bit of time that sucks, things'll get better. Jus' call me, Ok?"

I nod, trying to shake the mood. We finish our drinks and stagger out of the bar and over to Colfax. We flag down a cab, and Brad unsteadily climbs in, and leans his head back staring at the ceiling, eyes half open. The cabbie, an Egyptian, looks at him with a sour look.

"Just get him home ok," I smile at the cabbie. "He shouldn't be any trouble." I pass him one of the twenties that Brad had dropped in my cab. The cabbie takes the twenty, still looking like he had just tasted something foul. I waive to Brad as they drive off, then make an unsteady trail up Colfax to home.

I'm woken up at three thirty in the morning by my phone ringing. Grumbling I roll over to turn it off. I see that it's Brad and fumble to answer.

"What's up?" I croak and sit up.

"Hey, man," Brad sounds lost and confused, "where the fuck am I?"

"Fuck if I know," I snort, "I tossed your drunk ass in a cab about an hour and a half ago."

"Ok… but seriously, I have no idea where I'm at."

Maybe you're at Will's house, I think and grin a little.

"Find a street sign." I wait for a while, listening to him breath as he stumbles down the street.

"York and 40th"

"What the hell are you doing over there?"

"If I knew I wouldn't have called you," he says exasperatedly.

"Ok, ok," I think of what I can do and come up blank. "I think you're screwed, buddy. I doubt you can find a cab to flag down over there, and I seriously doubt one is going to come get you, and I am plastered, so there's no way I can come get you."

He's quiet for a moment, then laughs.

"So start walking, fucker, huh?"

"Yes, sir."

"Man, my wife's gonna be pissed. Now why don't we hang out any more?"

"Jeeze," I say laughing, "I don't know Brad."

"Yeah, see you later, brother."

"You got it, Brad."

"Call me, I was serious about that job."

"Of course," I reply, not quite sure if I will and not knowing why. I hang up, drop back to the bed and let the swirling of the night take me flowing down the river of dreams.

When I wake up the next day around noon I see his card sitting on my dining room table, centered in a large clear space amongst the detritus. Like I had pushed everything out of the way, and, in my drunken stupor, polished a little bit of the table and set the card center, as if to say : "Hey dumbass, there is a way out."

I ponder it as I drink my coffee and count my money from the night before. As I drop each twenty on the table, it flutters down, crisp and green, reminding me that I'd swore the night before to give Brad back his money. I ponder the dilemma over another cup of coffee, then scoop up the cash, leaving the card to gather dust in a clear circle on the table.

Blood on the Concrete

There's blood on the sidewalks today

Crimson splashed from tight-fisted pugilists

With scabs on their knuckles

And piss in their eyes

Blotches like Orion's belt

Burgundy and dried

Fallen

Dripped in a row

Telling a story

Of bourbon bruising

And passion rushed

Bloody knuckles

And broken teeth

A miasma hangs in the air

Alive with savage teeth

A Cheshire grin

With gristle jammed gums

Gleaming like a poison moon

So there's blood on the sidewalk

Rain will come tomorrow

To wash it away

PART 3

The summer's cooling off, the days getting shorter and Brad's card has gathered dust on my dining room table. I pull into a convenience store on the corner of Colfax and York and curse as I hit a pothole, hearing the suspension creak. I park, get out, and check my tires. The front driver's side tire is worn through to the steel radial interior. I had asked for a new one and had been told that they were out. Really? A cab company that does all of its own maintenance, out of tires? Right. I just hoped that it blew before winter so I could have at least one tire with tread on it. I also hoped that it didn't blow while I was doing seventy on the highway. It seemed a gamble, but there was nothing I could do about it except buy a new one with my own money, which I sure as hell wasn't about to do.

I walk into the convenience store and grab some nuts and a smoothie, walk back outside and get back into my cab. As I'm backing out a filthy looking man runs up to me, waiving his hands. Against my better judgment I stop and roll the window down.

"I need a ride to the airport!" It's one in the morning and he reeks of cheap alcohol, or maybe just plain rubbing alcohol. I turn away and start to back up again.

"I got money, man." I look back at him as he fans out a large number of twenties, grinning a gap-toothed smile. What the hell?

"Ok, get in, off we go to the airport."

"Great, great, you won't regret it," he says as he climbs into the back. I better not, I think. If I gun it, I can just make it out to the airport and back in time for the last call crowd. I leave the window rolled down as I catch a whiff of my passenger. He's definitely been living on the rough. I wonder where he got the money, but then realize that I don't care as long as he hasn't made it himself with a copier and highlight markers.

I turn down York and floor it, just making the light on Seventeenth. My passenger leans over the seat and I catch another heady gust of booze and body odor as he gabbles in my ear frantically.

"I'm going to fly down to Cali and surprise my sister." Something tells me that it's going to be a hell of surprise. I suddenly realize that there probably aren't any flights out of DIA at 1:30 in the morning, not to mention probably no one at the ticket counters. Even though I want the money, I find myself speaking up.

"Think there's going to be anyone at the airport to book a flight with?"

"Sure, sure, we're a twenty-four hour culture now, don't you know?" I feel his breath hot and rank on the side of my neck as I pull onto the on ramp for I-70. "I can buy a car, a meal, porno, a real woman, any fucking time, man! All I need is money, and I got fucking money, buddy!" He waives the wad of cash, and a twenty falls out of his fist to fly around the cab, he darts over the seat to grab it, and I swerve a bit as he bumps into me.

"Take it easy for fuck's sake," I shout over the breeze blowing in through the open window. I grab the twenty quickly and hand it to him, he waives me off.

"Keep it, as a tip," he laughs maniacally, "the money's for the taking, young man, this is fucking America!" I shrug and shove the bill into my pocket. If that's how he wants to play it, I don't care, although I do notice him stuffing the money into a pocket in one of his many jackets. "It's all about the goddamn money!" He leans back and howls. "I'm going to eat this fucking night my friend. Champaign and cigars and hot California pussy. After I see my sister, of course, my good man. Family comes first, family comes first." I feel him shuffle around behind me and glance in the mirror as he takes a pull off of a bottle of cheap vodka. He catches me looking and grins again, leaning over the seat. "Care for a pull of fine grain spirits, sir?"

"No," I say, laughing, getting into the spirit. "Gotta drive, gotta make that money!"

"Damn right," he leans back again and gazes out the window watching the buildings buzz by, "all of that, all the glitter and the dirt, it runs on money. " He takes another pull and speaks so quietly I barely hear him. "You just need to grab a piece of it." He drinks deep and sighs. "Just a little fucking piece."

I turn onto Pena, and he spends the rest of the trip in a contemplative silence. I pull up to the East Terminal, get out like a limo driver for a proper millionaire, and open the door for him. He pushes four crinkled twenties into my hand and winks at me.

"On to the next great adventure, good sir." He drains the rest of the bottle, goes to throw it in the back of the cab, then stops and looks at me questioningly. I nod and he gently tosses it to the floor.

"You're a good man," he says and reaches up and pats me on the cheek with a grubby hand, "don't forget that, no matter what happens, ok?"

"Sure," I reply, "have a good flight."

"Right," he says and straightens his outer jacket, "good night."

I watch him walk towards the doors at a veering angle, and tip my hat, chuckling. Looking around, I shrug and get into the cab. I have a feeling the man's adventures are about to get rough. Did they have a drunk tank at the airport? I don't know and don't want to find out. I pull on my seat belt and drive off towards the glow of civilization crawling up against the towering mountains, ready for my own next great adventure.

✿ ◉ ◎ ✿

It's a cool summer night, turning towards fall, where the wind blows off the Rockies and rolls through town, cooling it for once. I drive, with the windows rolled down, enjoying the freshness of the breeze. I just dropped a fare off near Stapleton, and I'm cruising down 20th when the tire finally blows. I curse a heady string of obscenities and pull over. It could have been worse. I could have been on the highway. It could have been during the bar rush. I could have been on my way to get a regular. There's a whole rainbow of could have been worse, but it still sucks. I call dispatch and tell them that the tire's blown and they tell me that they'll be there "soon" whatever that means. I walk around the cab and inspect the damage. I feel around back behind the tire and find that the whole tire is almost ripped off as I cut myself on the ragged metal of the exposed steel radials. Definitely good that it didn't happen on the highway, I would have been down to the rim in seconds. I wrap my finger in a paper napkin, get a book out and start to read when my phone rings. Figures. I answer.

"Hey, cowboy." It's Carrie and she pronounces the words carefully, slowly. She's obviously fucked up and in need of ride. Could have been worse, I think.

"What's up, Carrie?"

"I'm bad," she half sobs, "I'm in a bad way, cowboy, I need my knight in shining armor."

"I'm sorry," I respond, not sure if I am, "just blew a tire, gotta wait for the repair truck." She silent for a moment.

"How... how long?"

"I don't know," I think that the last thing I want to deal with is her fucked up mess. I come up with a number, "could be an hour or longer."

"Oh... well..." she's silent again, and, feeling horrible, I find myself wishing that she'll just blow the whole thing off, "just come get me when you can, ok? It's important."

"Sure, darling, sure," I reply, hating myself. Both for not wanting to get her and not being a dick enough to tell her so. She gives me the address and I go back to reading.

He shows up about forty five minutes later and changes the tire, whistling at the damage to the tire.

"Man, they should've changed this a while ago," he says, wiping his dirty hands on his stained overalls.

"Yeah," I reply restraining from ranting at the guy, it's not his fault the company sucks, "I told them, but..."

"Yep. Hear that a lot. It's gonna bite them in the ass someday."

He nods to me and gets into his truck. I get in the cab and book back in. There are no fares open in my zone, and I debate just blowing off Carrie. It's not like she'll have any money, and it doesn't sound like she was in any condition to be any fun. In the end, though, I just can't do it. Sighing, I put the cab in gear and head to go pick up Carrie.

The address is a rundown row house off of Welton. She's sitting on a low stone wall slumped against a tree, eyes half open. The sun has just started to set and she's half in shadow, half lit by red light. She moves weakly when I pull up.

"Shit," I mutter under my breath, put it in park and get out. I walk up to her, then crouch down in front of her. She looks at me listlessly, head wobbling, eyes narrowed.

"Hey," she croaks, then licks her lips.

"Hey yourself." I take her head in my hands gently as she nods forward, "How are you doing?"

"Been better," she snorts, "been better."

I shake my head and help her to her feet. She leans heavily

against me, and I half carry her to the cab. Even as dead weight, she strikes me as light, ephemeral, like carrying a broken bird. I go to place her in the front, and she shakes her head.

"No, inna back," she slurs, "I wanna lie down."

I lean her up against the cab and open the door, grabbing her as she starts to slide down. I gingerly lay her in the back, tucking her legs up as I close the door. I walk around, get in and fasten my seat belt.

"Where are we going?" I ask, half expecting her to ask me to stay at my place. She doesn't answer, and I sigh in exasperation. "Carrie," I start harshly, then stop as I see her. She's lying in an awkward pile, her face is so pale it's almost blue, and I can't tell if she's breathing. "Carrie!" I shout and open the door, choking and getting twisted up in the seat belt. I tear at the buckle and roll out the door, wrenching my shoulder on the seat belt. I finally untangle myself and yank the door open. I crawl in frantically and feel for a pulse. I don't feel anything, but what the fuck would I know? I'm probably checking the wrong spot. I lean in close to her mouth and listen for breath, I hear nothing and place my hand above her lips, looking to see if her chest is rising and falling. I feel nothing, and see nothing, and suddenly I smell the overwhelming stench of shit.

"Fuck, fuck fuck," I curse and recoil, back out of the cab, hand over my mouth. "Dead, she's fucking dead." I quickly shut the door and start the cab up. Hospital. There's a fucking hospital near here. I drive madly down the street and curse as I hit Welton and see the light rail speed by. I hammer my hands on the steering wheel, tears of frustration sprouting in my eyes. I gun it as soon as the train passes cutting off a minivan that honks. I'm driving like a madman, and this area of Denver is a nightmare of one way streets and odd angles, and I'm forced to back track.

"It's Ok, Carrie," I find myself say, almost cooing, "we're almost there baby." I wipe tears off of my face as I turn on Downing and gun it, running the red light at 20th and pull into the ER roundabout. I slam it into park, feeling the cab rock up on its suspension and lurch out of the cab. I run around to the passenger side, and pull her out by her legs, tossing her over my shoulder in a fireman's carry, ignore the smell, and half run, half stumble to the doors. My arrival has already gotten the attention of the ER nurses and I have a reception waiting for me. They grab her, toss her on gurney and start CPR. One of the nurses pulls me aside, while I stare at her helplessly.

"What can you tell me?"

I look at him confused. "What?"

"About her," he looks over my shoulder at the cab. "Do you know what happened? Do you know her?"

"Um," trying to focus, "drugs, pretty sure it's drugs."

"Ok, good, do you know what kind?"

"No," I look around bewildered, "I don't know, maybe heroin."

"Ok," he puts his hand on my arm, "just go sit down for a moment."

"But," I say vaguely pointing to my cab, "what about my cab?"

"You're in no condition to drive right now. The cab'll be just fine there for now."

Numbly, I nod and take a seat. He comes by later and sits down next to me, I can tell by the look in his face and I take a deep shuddering breath.

"I'm sorry, there's nothing we could do." I nod jerkily. "Did you know her?"

"Yes," I start, "No. She was regular." I look down and realize I'm holding my hat in my hands, kneading the brim. I smooth it a bit, run my hand through my hair and put it back on.

"Ok," he says, "the police are going to have to ask a few questions, routine stuff, can you handle that?" I'm struck by the kindness in his voice and nod woodenly. A cop comes over and asks me a few questions. Nothing too probing, he doesn't seem too worried about the whole situation. He asks to see the cab and I lead him outside. It seems unreal, like I'm encased in cotton. The cop's words come from far away as I open the back. He peers in and then leans back quickly.

"Whoa, you're going to want to wash that out, I think." I nod again, head encased in unreality. He takes my information, hands me his card and tells me to call him if I think of anything. I nod woodenly again and get into the cab. I sit there for a moment, dazed, then calmly pull out of the roundabout and into the parking lot. I drive distractedly for a while, ignoring the beeping of my computer and the call for fares. I find myself in a car wash, cab running, spray nozzle in hand, hosing out the inside of my cab. Water puddles in the bottom of the car, and I sop it up with rags bought from a machine. I squeeze the fetid rags out again and again, until the water is gone, then throw them in a heap. I take the spray nozzle and hit my hands. The power washer stings and opens cuts my hands, making them red and spotted. I drop it on the ground, back up against the wall and sink to my haunches, ass on the ground, water soaking through my pants and begin to cry. It comes in great racking sobs. I hold my ribs tight, head down and twitch.

I stay this way for a while, listening to the hum of the engine over my cry, almost silent now. I suck in a deep gasping breath, and get to my feet. I pick my hat up from the ground, shake the water off of it, get in and drive. I turn the computer off and drive aimless through the Denver night, shivering from my wet clothes, and finally drive home. I park, and walk up the stairs to my house, leaving the door open. I strip my clothes off on the way up the stairs, leaving a trail of sodden shit-stained garments. Naked, I pour myself a strong whiskey and get in the shower. Leaning against the cool wall, I let the hot water run off me, and cycle into the drain. Still naked, I pour myself another drink, and sit on my bed, back to the wall, staring at nothing.

✿◉◎✿

I sit on my porch and stare at the cab, feeling the money drain away. I wonder how long I can go without driving before they start calling me or if they'd just come and get it and then take me to court. I'm sure there's a procedure, and I'm sure I don't care. After about twenty minutes of pointless wondering, I get up and head to the liquor store.

I can taste the booze on my breath from the night before and I'm positive that I smell something awful, my breath a wind of whiskey. When I rub my eyes, the sweat on my fingers burns them, and I know that I should sober up and get driving. But I just can't face the cab, the people, any of it. The walk to the liquor store on the corner is a herculean effort, with the sun beating down on my neck, heating up my clothes, forcing my already parched body to push out small beads of sweat. I consider an air conditioned bar, but reject the idea right away. I just can't see dealing with people at all, I feel horrible, hunchbacked and misanthropic. If I hadn't drunk all the whiskey the night before, sitting in my bedroom in the dark shaking, there's no way that I'd leave the house. I open the door of the liquor store and revel in the blast of coolness as I go inside. The old Korean lady is working the counter, and I nod as I walk to the coolers and grab a six pack of beer. I set it on the counter and she tilts her head and smiles at me.

"No work today, cab man?"

"No," I feel a lump in my throat and fight it down, "just can't do it today. How about a fifth of some cheap whiskey?" I point vaguely to the plastic bottle row behind her, and she turns.

"Ten High?"

"Why not." Between the flat tire and… Carrie, I was pretty broke. Counting out singles with shaking hands, I realize that I have to go back to work just so I can keep on drinking. I pay her, take my change and march back to my house like a zombie. Work. That's a conversation for another day. Tomorrow most likely. I close all of the curtains, turn the TV on to bad daytime programming and pour myself a tall glass of cheap whiskey. On the rocks with a dash of water. I remember the beer and crack one open as well. Time to get started. The day falls into night, and things get spotty:

A flash in the blackness of me crying silently on the couch watching a rerun of an eighties sit com.

A beer bottle smashing into the wall and glass flying.

A punched hole in the wall. Split knuckles and blood.

A piercing pain in my foot as I step on the broken beer bottle.

The world spinning as I fall into my bed a maelstrom of blood, sorrow and anger.

❀ ◉ ◎ ◉ ❀

I wake up with a splitting headache, not sure if it's day or night. I'm fully dressed lying across my bed with a half full beer in my hand. I take a sip and regret it, the warm flat beer makes my stomach lurch and I stagger upright, then almost fall as the pain in my foot slams up my leg. I groan and hop to the bathroom, banging my knee as I collapse in front of the toilette and start dry heaving bile and stomach acid. I cough, eyes watering and lean against the bathroom wall, panting and making quiet animal sounds. I see a track of bloody footprints coming down the hallway and into my room. I reach down and pull my foot onto my lap, craning my head to see the sole. It's a bloody mess of scabs and dirt.

I haul myself upright slowly, stomach still churning, and hop to the bathtub. I turn the water on and stick my foot under the water, wincing as it pours over it. I slowly raise the temperature until it's as hot as I can stand and grit my teeth as the caked blood washes off. I grab a towel and dry my foot off, then sit on the floor and awkwardly try to see how much glass is in the bottom of my foot. I can't see any glass, but there are four small slices in the arch of my foot. I hop up and pull out my first aid kit, smear some antibacterial gel on the cuts and wrap my foot in gauze.

I grab some cleanish socks and put them painfully on, then hop downstairs, carefully avoiding the broken glass in front of the stairs. I go into the living room and stop in shock. It looks as if I had invited a frat house over the night before. The sofa cushions are scattered around the room, there's another pile of broken glass on the far side of the room, the whiskey bottle is empty, and there are three holes in the wall. I look down at my hand and see that it's scuffed with little red scabs across my knuckles.

I flex it experimentally, and it's stiff, but it doesn't feel like anything is broken. Small miracles. If I had broken it, I don't know what I would have done, it's not like the cab company offers a health plan. I pick up a cushion, put it on the couch, and sit down. I grab my boots and take a deep breath before pulling one on over my damaged foot. I let out an involuntary wincing breath as the pain hits me, then lean back. I could use some pain killers, but they're upstairs and there's no way I can make that trip. I lean forward and run my hands through my hair, then grab my cowboy hat and limp out the door to my cab.

My first stop is the corner convenience store for gum, aspirin and water. The walk in and back to the cab are almost all I can take I sit in the cab for a moment, breathing heavily, then pop the cap on the water and down a couple of pills I gulp down half the liter, feeling the ice cold water hit my stomach like a hammer. I wince and breathe deep then put four sticks of gum in my mouth. I'm still a little drunk and pretty sure that booze stench is wafting off of me in palpable waves, like stink lines in a cartoon. Feeling as together as I can, I head out to the cab company.

I limp in, sunglasses still on, ignoring the glances, and pay what I have left in my wallet on my lease. Luckily, if you can say that, Carrie died on a Friday, and my lease was mostly paid off. I leave twenty on my lease and shrug.

"Bad night?" The girl behind the counter asks. I snort, not sure if I want to laugh or cry.

"You could say that," my voice comes out rough and gravelly, scrapped raw from whiskey and vomit.

"What happened?" she asks. I find that I'm leaning heavily on the counter. For once I'm glad there's that layer of impersonal glass between us.

"Nothing," I shake my head, "personal stuff." I couldn't even imagine tell her what happened, and wonder briefly if the cab company wants me to fill out a report or something. Damned if I'd do it though, they'd probably ground my cab, and have me come in at seven am to watch a video titled Death in the Backseat: Why Suzie isn't Breathing Anymore. I point to the money. "Is that enough to turn me back on?"

"Sure," she says looking on the computer, "I'll just roll it over to next weeks, but you need to pay it off as soon as possible, if you let it roll over next week, they'll shut you off."

"Sure," I say, taking my printout, "thanks."

I limp back to my cab, get in, and stare at the mountains for a while. Willing myself to move, to turn on the cab, to start up the computer. Anything. I'm frozen, all but my hands that flutter and shake on the steering wheel. Vibrating like fragile birds, they float up to my face. I find tears on my face and wipe them away. Almost of their own volition, my hands start the car and log me in. I turn onto Elm and drive over to MLK, waiting for the first bell of the evening. I tell myself that I'll work until I get a hundred and twenty, then call it.

The first bell is a long time coming, and I find myself driving restlessly, sickness gnawing at my gut, pain throbbing from my foot. The streets are empty and I feel alone, like the last man in the world, cruising restlessly through the growing night. Finally the computer pings and I take the bell without looking. It's in the Governor's Park neighborhood, and, like in a dream, I turn down Josephine and float by City Park, East High and the Botanic Gardens to Eighth.

They come rolling out of the building, drunk and rowdy, decked head to toe in Rocky's gear. I wasn't aware there was game going on and it boded well, especially for a Sunday. I feel the scabs crack on my foot and the blood begin to seep through the bandage as I turn down Washington. Their drunken banter hits my hangover like a hammer. I keep quiet and hope they'll leave me alone as I steer my way downtown. I drop them at the stadium and fight my way through game day traffic back to the hill. I get one more ballpark run, then a random run to the Highlands. I'm about to turn onto Speer when I get a bell for 14th and Federal. Cursing, I turn onto Speer, then into a parking lot. I turn around in the parking lot, then jet across three lanes of traffic into the turn lane, hitting the turn light onto Federal as it turns yellow. My car drifts a bit as I hit the corner a bit too fast. I brake a bit, then correct and head down Federal, feeling a slight spike of adrenaline.

The call is at a rundown motel that looks like it hasn't been updated since the seventies. The sign reads "Weekly and Monthly Rates" and I wonder what kind of shit fare I'm getting myself into. I squeeze through the tightly packed parking lot, noticing that a couple of the cars are up on blocks. Maybe they also have yearly rates. I pull up in front of room 114 and a wild eyed man in a dirty white t-shirt comes out. He yanks open the passenger door, and I move my stuff out of the way. He plops down and turns to me, giving me a glass-eyed stare, his breath reeks of cigarettes and vomit. Great.

"How ya doin', man?"

"Fine," I reply, wondering if I can ditch this fare, "where we going?"

"Downtown," he pulls out a large wad of crinkled twenties and tosses one on my lap. "Don't worry, man, I got money."

"Downtown it is." I back out through the narrow parking lot, make a three point turn, and pop the meter on.

"Don't worry about the meter, man, I'll pay you good." He tosses another twenty in my lap.

"Whatever you want," I say laughingly, and turn off the meter, "but put on your seatbelt, don't want a ticket."

"You got it boss," he pulls the seat belt on, hands shaking. We make quite a pair. I wait for traffic, then make a left on Federal, and another one down the ramp and onto West Colfax. He leans heavily against the window as we zoom down the ramp, then rolls it down and pukes.

"Sorry, boss," he says, half-heartedly wiping his lips as a little string of puke and drool snake down onto his stained t-shirt. "I just drove straight from Saint Louis," he tosses another twenty on my lap. "I'm a little tweaked out, need a beer and some titties, know what I mean?"

"Sure do." I snatch the cash up and stuff it in my pocket. "Titty bar?"

"Yeah, man, just the thing, nothing crappy though, I want to see some class act pussy, OK?"

"Know just the place." I pass Speer and turn towards downtown and pull up in front of a high end strip club. "This is the best in town." He looks it up and down and miles.

"Here," he hands me two more twenties, "looks perfect man. Gimmie your number, so I can get a ride back."

"Sure," I hand him my card, and he gets out of the cab. I watch him lurch up to the club and yank the door open. I suddenly have this image of him stumbling into a high end strip joint, wild eyed with vomit on his shirt, and gun it out of there.

A few minutes later, my phone starts ringing, but I ignore it. The gnawing pain in my gut has turned to raw hunger. I try to remember the last time I ate, and come up with a big blank. I head back up to Federal and grab a couple of burritos, then hit a liquor store and get a twelve pack and a fifth of whiskey. My phone rings a few more times, but I'm heading home with a boot full of blood, a bag full of burritos, a six pack and a bottle of whiskey.

I limp up the steps and into my living room. I look at my phone guiltily and then pick it up and check the message.

"Um," a cultured voice says, "I do believe you just dropped a fare off here, and we would appreciate if you would come back and retrieve him." I hear yelling in the background. I erase the message and the following three without listening to them. I think about going and getting him, but realize that I'm just not in the mood to deal with that mess. There's no telling how the night would go, I'm sure I'd make a ton of money, but have a feeling that it just might end up with the police at some point. The adventure is there, but the spirit is weak. Besides, he's either gotten another cab or gone to jail by now.

I pull of my boot and peel off the blood-soaked sock. I should probably go get stitches. But instead, I crack a beer and wolf down a burrito.

I polish off the burritos and beers, feeling mildly queasy, I look at the bottle of whiskey with a strange mixture of hatred and longing. The food has soaked up most of the beer, and I feel my hangover recede a bit, but not enough. It's sitting, taught and brutal, right under the beer buzz, a feral thing, just waiting to go for my throat and shake me in my misery. Hands still shaking slightly, I twist the cap, hearing the cracking of the plastic safety ring like a gunshot in my silent cavernous house. I limp to the kitchen, rinse out a dirty glass, and grab a tray of ice cubes, then settle onto the couch. The amber gold of cheap whiskey mutes the tumble and tinkle of ice in the finger stained glass as I pour up to the brim, surrendering to the inevitability of the night. Hand still shaking slightly despite the beer and food, I bring the bright glass of death to my lips and sip, release a heartfelt sigh as the whiskey burns my throat. A warm psalm to misery as it hits my stomach and warms the cold hackles of my heart.

❀ ◎ ◎ ◎ ❀

An hour and half and half a bottle of whiskey later, I find myself still sitting on the couch, numb, staring at the blood streaked dent in the wall where my fist hit in the half remembered madness of the night before. The anger has been replaced, it seems by an odd listless complacency, like I'm floating. I reach up and realize that I'm crying, that my face is soaked and covered with salt, that I haven't moved in an hour. There's no TV on, no music. I just sit in a dim room with an empty glass in my hand. I should fill the glass with whiskey and the melted ice from the ice cube trays, I should get up and go to the bathroom. I should find the remote and turn on the TV. I should do something, anything, a voice screams in the back of my head, instead of just wallowing, just floating and broken.

My phone rings and snaps me out of my trance. I set my glass down and pick it up, meaning to kill the call, but my stumble-drunk hands answer it. It's Jod., I pause, pick my words carefully, stress them, make sure my mouth makes the right sounds in the right order. It seems as if I'm talking from the bottom of a deep well.

"Hey. Jody. How are. You?" I realize, from far away, that my voice is strangely stilted, robotic.

"Hey, are you ok?" Her voice is warm, a comforting buzz in my ear.

"Um," I feel a melting, a torrent coming. I take a shaky breathe, "No, no I don't think I am."

"What's the matter?"

"She's dead." I see it again, and remember how frail and tiny she felt in my arms, like she weighed nothing, was made of tissue paper.

"What? Who's dead?"

The words start flowing, a final shattering of the ice, a purge of bile and pus, and I tell her everything. When the tidal flow of words stops, she says three words, clear as a bell:

"I'm coming over." Then she hangs up, and I stare at the phone like it's something new, something different, a lifeline perhaps. Then, in a shock, I look around my house. The glass on the floor, the dent in the wall, the beer cans and burrito wrappers, and the trail of blood leading up the stairs. In a solid panic, I hop up and try to make some sort of order out of the chaos, not sure if that'll be possible.

When she arrives forty five minutes later, I've cleaned up what I can, and hung a picture crookedly over the holes. It isn't quite large enough so little curls of drywall paper peek around the frame, like a psychotic strip tease. I sit on the couch, waiting, and pour myself another glass of whiskey. To sooth my nerves, to fortify my will, I tell myself. Not to calm the quiet terror deep inside, knowing that she's coming over. Not to quell the mad laughter, the fear of even the possibility of connecting with another human being again. My hand twitches and spills a little dribble down my chin; I wipe it on my arm and try to sit absolutely still. If you don't move, I think, life can't get you, can't drag you down, can't rip you down to die choking on your own vomit and covered in shit in the back seat of a cab driven, in all reality, by a complete stranger. Still, just be still, I will be an ice sculpture titled Drunk in Stillness. I'm so concentrated on staying still that I almost forget that she's coming over, I'm startled by the knock on the door, almost angry at getting pulled from my stillness. I get up and limp to the door.

"What's a matter with your foot?" She asks. I look down dumbly, and see that I'm still leaving little dots of blood on the floor.

"Um, cut it on glass," I say and give a kind of dumbass shrug.

"Christ," she shakes her head, more bemused than disgusted. "Well, sit down then." I limp over and sit down on the couch. She stands for a moment hands on hips, looking down at me.

"You're a mess, and I don't think you need any more of this." She grabs the bottle of whiskey and heads to the kitchen. I start to protest, then think better of it. I am a mess, and I know it. She comes back with a glass and sits down next to me, I feel hopeful for a moment, and then she drinks half of it in one gulp.

"I didn't say that I didn't need some of it," she slams the rest of the glass and turns to me. "Now, let's see about that foot, where's that first aid kit you had last time I was over here?"

"Upstairs, in the bathroom." She nods and leaves the room. I look at the empty glass and the amber dusting of whiskey still at the bottom. I think of licking it, getting that last drop. I decide against it, it wouldn't do to have her come down the stairs and see me tonguing the glassware.

She returns and has me pull of my sock. She kneels before me in an unknowing parody of the last time she was in my house, with rolls reversed. She cleans my foot, and I try not to look at the soft curves of her cleavage being tugged up by a white bra. She reaches for a bandage and catches me looking/not looking and smiles. She gets up and goes to the kitchen to wash her hands. She comes back with two glasses.

"I guess one more won't hurt," she sets down the glasses on the coffee table, "for either of us." She takes a slow sip and sits down next to me, close. I can feel the heat off of her, and where her thigh touches mine. "Now," she sets the glass down, "tell me about her." I hesitate, what did I really know about her?

"I really didn't know her that well, she was a regular, and sometimes, we'd, um..."

"Have sex?" She seems more amused than shocked, and I shrug my dumbass shrug again.

"Yes, not every time, but sometimes," I pick the drink up and take a sip, the gesture around the room, "she stayed over one time, when she had nowhere else to go." I take another drink and laugh shakily. "I'm pretty sure she stole my change jar."

"What happened?" She touches my hand.

"She," I drink deeply and put the glass down, "she just died... Od'd, I guess... I'm sure. She called me, seemed OK, if a little wasted, like most of my fairs, and then she was way out of it when I picked her up and then..." I feel it like a wave, building, "she died, alone. And when I picked her up, she," the wave breaks and I'm sobbing. "She was so, so light, like she was made of string and feathers and air." That's what keeps coming back to me; the smell of shit and vomit, and how light she was. I'm crying. Full wracking sobs. And Jodi holds me, runs her hand on my face, softly, and somehow we're kissing, and I notice that her cheeks are wet as well, and I'm not sure if it's from my face. We tangle and tear our clothes, a strange passion for the dead. No, not for the dead, a passion that we're alive. That through some accident we're alive, and they're dead, and that feeds us, as the clothes come off and we kiss each other's bodies. Slate our pain like thirst in each other, in our sweat and saliva and tears, slick and sad.

❀◉◉◉❀

I dream I'm floating, a teasing feeling in the back of my mind, like swaying in the branches of a tree. I wake up slowly, uncomfortably aware of Jodi in the bed next to me as my body wakes me to the strange sensation of another breathing body in my bed. I remember the clumsy if frantic love making the night before, on the couch, then later in my bed, until we were both sated and tired. I had dropped off to sleep holding her like I was drowning. I lie on my back for a moment, staring at the ceiling, my head throbbing. But like it's happing to someone else. The pain in my foot throbs, far away as well. I hear her sigh, and I roll over to see her staring at me intently. Her eyes are blue, flecked with brown, I notice for the first time.

"Hi," she says quietly.

"Hi," I say back, not sure what to say, "last night…"

She cuts my off with a quick hand on my lips.

"Later," she sits up, holding the covers to her chest, "we'll talk about that later." She looks around, embarrassed. "Um, where are my clothes?" I look around and shrug.

"Downstairs, I think." She frowns and looks uncertain, her awkwardness makes me aware of my nakedness, and I fish a pair of jeans off the floor and pull them on under the covers. "I'll go get them."

"No, your foot…" I wave her off gruffly.

"Its fine," I stand up and do my best not to hobble out of the room. My throat is sand dry, and my head feels like it's stuffed with cotton, but I feel amazingly well considering the extent of the binge I've been on. I hop down the steps and grab whatever clothes of hers that I can find, hoping it's everything. I go back upstairs and drop them on the bed. I hesitate, then grab a shirt from the pile and put it on.

"I'll, I'll just go make some coffee, ok?"

"Thanks," she sounds relieved that I didn't stay and watch her dress, although part of me wants to. I go downstairs and put a pot of coffee on.

I'm sitting at the cluttered dining room table staring at Brad's card, when she comes down, running her fingers through her hair. I watch, looking at the nape of her neck as she pulls her hair back into a ponytail. She catches me looking and smiles shyly.

"Coffee?"

"Right there," I point to the kitchen counter, "there's a clean cup next to it and some milk and sugar, wasn't sure how you take it."

"Thanks." She pours herself a cup and I watch her as the light from the window casts a shadow across her back, and imagine... Then I stop myself. She turns and sees me looking, I don't look away.

"Last night-" I start again.

"It's complicated," she says, and looks down as she stirs her coffee. She looks back up looking small and scared. "I haven't been with anyone since-"

"Oh!" I take a quick gulp of coffee. "Look-" I stand up and walk into the kitchen. She's looking down at her coffee. I set mine down, and take her chin in my fingertips. I gently lift her chin up and make her look me in the eye.

"Last night-" she starts this time.

"Was complicated," I say and kiss her lightly on the forehead, "we'll figure it out, one way or the other, ok?" She nods and I pick my coffee back up and lean against the counter, whishing I could come up with something, anything to lighten the mood. We'd just spent the night making love and we're acting like we're at a funeral. In a way, we are. There's the specter of Ted right between us in the kitchen, almost like a physical presence, and for the first time in a long time, I remember how much I miss him. Just hanging out on the back porch drinking beer and talking home improvement. So fucking normal, so fucking comfortable. With Jodi for him to go back to, slightly drunk, and with Mary for me to go home to. I don't know how Jodi can stand it, being cut off like that, being so alone.

"Come on, let's sit down," Jodi says, and touches my arm, light as a feather. We sit down at the table and Jodi clears a small space, looking at the receipts and the crazy scribbled notes. She picks up one blank credit card slip and reads aloud.

"There's blood on the sidewalks today/Crimson splashed from tight-fisted pugilists/With scabs on their knuckles/And piss in their eyes." She raises and eyebrow sardonically, an unasked question. I think of trying to explain the need that comes welling up with the words. The mad desire to scribble them down obsessively on whatever's handy, and I'm at a loss. Instead I shrug.

"Guess I'm turning into a poet or writing a song or something."

"Pretty dark song."

"The best ones are," I try to say lightly, feeling unreasonably defensive.

"It's ok," she laughs, picking up another one, "I think they're good, and probably good for you." She sets it down and looks at me steadily. I'm uncomfortable, caught in her measuring gaze, but I don't look away. "My, oh, my, what are we going to do with you?" She says methodically. She finishes her coffee in a quick gulp and sighs gustily, then gets up and walks over to me. She bends down and kisses me on the forehead then straightens up, looking down on me with a wistful smile pulling the corners of her mouth.

"It's like you're in Limbo. Stuck, between what was and what will be. I mean, look at how you're living." She waves her arm, encompassing the wreck of my living room, the shambles of my yard, the note strewn table, the piles of clothing around my mattress sitting on the floor in my bedroom... the vacant room where my son used to sleep. The gesture takes it all in, then her hand rests on my cheek. "You've got to do something- sell the house, get roommates, something. You're living in between, isolated, even your job. You're just an interruption in people's lives." She crouches down and takes my hands in hers, looking up at me. "I like you, I really do, but you gotta figure your shit out, baby." She stands up and kisses me again. "I'll probably be here when you do, but you never know." With that, she turns, grabs her bag and her bra off of the couch and walks out the house. When the door opens it frames her in shining morning light, a silhouette of soft curves framed by brightness. The door bangs shut and I sit at the cluttered table, coffee going cold, eyes burning with my last vision of her.

❀ ◉ ◎ ❀

I'm in my cab, a few weeks later, the sun is setting, and I've sat my book down, too dark to read. I think about Jodi, and what she said. I know deep in my heart that I'm hanging on to the house because somehow I think that Mary will be back, bring my boy back to me, and we'll be happy again. The house will fill with light and laughter and joy. I know it's not going to happen, Mary's made that more than clear, but I still can't let go of the house.

Carrie is still there, dying in the back of my cab, in the late nights, when I'm all alone. I think of Jodi's skin against me, warm and enticing, and sigh. I haven't heard from her since that night, although I've left a few messages. Not too many, I hope. I don't want to cross the line between wanting to see her again and stalking her. And I do want to see her again. But she's right, I do need to make some choices, just man up and make them, but they seem so distant. I start to put my cab in gear, just to drive, and my phone rings. I answer it, and the voice, oddly familiar, sounds like its coming from another planet, crackling and hissing.

"My good cabbie, how fair you?"

"Um, fine?" I answer, a bit confused. I can almost place the strange cadence.

"Wonderful, wonderful." The voice pauses and I swear I can hear him gulp down a drink. "My business in California has gone most well. I was wondering if you were, perhaps, free to get me from the airport. The cab drivers out here are cretins one and all." Suddenly, I remember the drunken ragged man with the large wad of cash and bottle of cheap booze.

"Why, not?" I say laughing. "I'll be there in twenty five minutes, good sir," joining in the fun, "meet me on the East Concourse, departures area."

"Excellent, I look forward to it, my fine man."

I hang up, shaking my head, and drive towards Colorado Boulevard. Some days, it just takes the right fare. My cab floats, light as a feather, as I hit seventy on the highway. For once, it's clear to Pena as I ease the gentle curve off of the highway. It had rained earlier, and, as the sun sets, a rare fog comes out to grace the Colorado night. I revel in driving, the simplicity of just driving. Decisions can come tomorrow, tonight I'll revel in the in between, the undecided. The night can bring anything, riches, laughter, madness.

So, for now, I just drive, my headlights splitting the night, a line between dark and light. I drive. Through drifting fog and summer's end out onto the plains. I drive. To the floating lights of the airport, an island in the mist, to wherever the night will take me, I drive.

CPSIA information can be obtained
at www.ICGtesting.com
Printed in the USA
FSOW01n0925170617
35311FS